G #   G June
I #   2 July.

CRYSTAL OSCILLATOR CIRCUITS

Four quartz crystal oscillators operating at 1, 40, 58.3, and 109 MHz.

CRYSTAL OSCILLATOR CIRCUITS

Robert J. Matthys

A Wiley-Interscience Publication

JOHN WILEY & SONS

New York   Chichester   Brisbane   Toronto   Singapore

Library of Congress Cataloging in Publication Data:

Matthys, Robert J., 1929–
    Crystal oscillator circuits.

    "A Wiley-Interscience publication."
    Bibliography: p.
    Includes index.
    1. Oscillators, Crystal.   I. Title.

TK7872.07M37 1983   621.3815'33   82-17564
ISBN 0-471-87401-9

Printed in the United States of America

10 9 8 7 6 5 4 3 2 1

PREFACE

Crystal oscillators are widely used in computers, microprocessors, frequency and time standards, transmitters, receivers, and many digital circuits and electronic instruments. The performance of a crystal oscillator is highly dependent on its circuit design, and many different types of circuits are in use—each with its good and bad points. Some work better that others; some are designed for low cost and some for maximum frequency stability; others to interface with digital logic circuitry.

This book responds to the need to analyze all types of solid-state crystal oscillator circuits according to how they work, how to design them, and which ones work best. Both fundamental oscillators from 1 kHz to 20 MHz and VHF harmonic oscillators from 20 to 100 MHz are covered. Many new circuits that have not appeared in publications before are included.

The circuits have been divided into two categories: discrete transistor and integrated circuits. Discrete transistor circuits offer more circuit possibilities than do ICs. Discrete transistors permit a wider control over circuit design and, in general, have less time delay in the amplifier. Discrete transistors are used for all but one of the VHF harmonic oscillators, which are treated as a separate subgroup. In order to match digital voltage and impedance requirements, most discrete oscillator circuits require a buffer interface circuit if they are to be used with digital circuitry. On the other hand, integrated-circuit oscillators are primarily intended to be used with digital logic circuitry and, in general, will interface easily with it.

Chapter 1 gives a short history of oscillator circuit development. Chapter 2 describes the electrical characteristics of quartz crystals from a circuit design standpoint. Chapter 3 covers the fundamentals of oscillator operation, describes the basic ways of connecting a crystal into a circuit, and derives analytically the crystal's response to being driven with a square wave.

Chapter 4 describes the six most important design characteristics for an oscillator circuit. Chapter 5 lists basic circuit types and describes how each one works. In-circuit Q and short-term frequency stability are covered experimentally and analytically in Chapters 6 and 7, which show that both Q and frequency stability are controlled by the external load on the crystal, and that good short-term stability can be obtained with either high or low load resistance values, but not with intermediate values.

A working oscillator circuit of each type is given in Chapters 10 and 11, together with waveform photographs and comments on each circuit's strong and weak points. Chapter 10 covers discrete transistor types while Chapter 11 covers the IC types. Chapter 12 compares the performance of the different circuits, and points out that the Pierce and modified Meacham circuits give the best performance. Chapter 13 has information on how to select your own oscillator circuit.

This book involved a considerable amount of experimental effort. To control the effort, an arbitrary limit was placed on all circuits by requiring them to operate from a single +5 VDC supply. Every well-known or potentially worth-while circuit type that the author is aware of or has used in many years of circuit design is included here. The older vacuum tube circuits have been converted to their more modern transistor equivalents.

ROBERT J. MATTHYS

Minneapolis, Minnesota
January 1983

ACKNOWLEDGMENT

In a work such as this, one always stands on the shoulders of one's forebears. I particularly want to acknowledge the work of Don Firth at Magnavox Corporation. His oscillator handbook pointed out several key circuit design issues in a crystal oscillator, particularly the voltage divider concept of a crystal's internal series resistance with its external load resistance and the significance of the ratio of the crystal's external load resistance to its internal series resistance.

R. J. M.

CONTENTS

ix

CRYSTAL OSCILLATOR CIRCUITS

CHAPTER ONE

BACKGROUND

Crystal oscillators were invented in the 1920s. Cady made one of the first ones in 1921. Miller patented both his own and Pierce's circuits in 1930 [1]. Pierce patented both his own and Miller's circuits in 1931 [2], and after some legal arguing in the courts, Pierce repatented both circuits again in 1938 [3]. Sabaroff's quartz crystal version of the Colpitts LC oscillator was published in 1937 [4], and Meacham's resistance bridge circuit was published in 1938 [5]. Butler published his article on VHF harmonic oscillators in 1946 [6]. Goldberg and Crosby published their article on cathode coupled or grounded grid oscillators in 1948 [7].

The U.S. Army Signal Corps funded an intense quartz crystal development program during and after World War II and funded a small amount of oscillator circuit development along the way. Edson did a study of VHF harmonic oscillator circuits in 1950 [8] and published his classic book on vacuum tube oscillators of all types in 1953 [9]. In 1965, Firth published his design handbook [10] on the Pierce circuit and the Butler common base harmonic circuit.

The early oscillators used vacuum tubes, which had limited life and were, therefore, high-maintenance items. Consequently, there was a considerable advantage in using a one-tube oscillator circuit, as compared with a two-tube circuit. Strong emphasis was placed on getting the maximum power out of the oscillator circuit, since this meant that fewer power amplifier tubes were required in a transmitter. Vacuum tubes operated at power supply voltages of 150–300 VDC, which permitted large voltage swings and made it extremely easy to overdrive the crystal's dissipation limit or even fracture the crystal.

With the advent of transistor and IC circuits, the emphasis was placed on performance. Transistors are very small and have indefinite life, so in many cases, the number of transistors used in an oscillator circuit is al-

1

most irrelevant. The lower power supply voltage used in transistor circuits has reduced the crystal overdrive problem to more manageable proportions. And to get better frequency stability, oscillator circuits are now routinely designed with low power output, since it costs so little to add an amplifier stage.

CHAPTER TWO

QUARTZ CRYSTALS

This chapter covers the electrical characteristics of quartz crystals from a circuit design standpoint. For information on their mechanical characteristics or on the manufacturing process, the reader is referred to any standard text on quartz crystals.

Quartz exhibits a piezoelectric effect, that is, applying a voltage to the opposing surfaces of a piece of properly oriented quartz will make it change shape mechanically (and vice versa). A quartz crystal is a small, thin piece of quartz with two opposite surfaces metallized to make electrical connections. Its physical dimensions are tightly controlled since they control oscillation frequency.

Although there are many crystal cuts, at high frequencies (1 MHz and above), the one most commonly used is the AT cut. An AT-cut crystal is a thin piece of quartz with two parallel or slightly convex surfaces, usually about the size of a nickel or less. Electrical connections are made to the crystal by metallizing the two parallel faces on opposite sides of the crystal. The crystal's resonant frequency is inversely proportional to the crystal's thickness between these two metallized surfaces. Applying a voltage between the two metallized surfaces causes the AT crystal to move sideways internally in a thickness shear movement, as shown in Fig. 2.1. The traditional equivalent circuit using lumped constant elements for the crystal is shown in Fig. 2.2. Inductance L_x and series capacitance C_x represent the crystal's frequency-sensitive elements. Capacitance C_0 is the capacitance between the two metallized surfaces used as electrode contacts on the crystal and runs about 3–15 pF for most crystals.

The series resistance R_s of a typical crystal of any type of cut varies from about 10 Ω at 20 MHz, to a few hundred ohms at 1 MHz, up to a few thousand ohms at 100 kHz, and up to 200,000 Ω at 1 kHz. Table 2.1

3

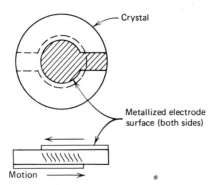

Figure 2.1. Shear motion of an AT-cut crystal at fundamental resonance.

shows some measured values of L_x, C_x, C_0, and R_s for several crystals.

The lowest fundamental frequency available in a quartz crystal is about 1 kHz. The highest fundamental frequency is about 20–25 MHz, above which the crystal becomes too thin and delicate to be handled. Oscillation can be continued to about 200 MHz by operating the crystal on its third, fifth, seventh, or ninth harmonic. A crystal's series resistance increases with the harmonic, from about 40 Ω at 20 MHz to about 200 Ω at 200 MHz.

Figure 2.3 shows the maximum series resistance of quartz crystals over a frequency range of 1 kHz–200 MHz. These data are taken from several specifications, so more than one limit is shown at some frequencies. A typical crystal will have about two-thirds the maximum resistance specified in Fig. 2.3. This wide variation in series resistance from 10 to 200,000 Ω is the largest single factor in oscillator design and dominates the design of every oscillator circuit.

Figure 2.4 shows the maximum drive power that can be put into a crystal without excessive heating and frequency shift in the crystal. Figure 2.5 shows the maximum permissible drive voltage across the crystal *at exact series resonance*. Figure 2.5 is derived from the series resistance and maximum power data given in Figs. 2.3 and 2.4. Figures 2.3–2.5 apply to crystals of all common types of cuts mounted in a gas-filled container. Note that in Fig. 2.5 the maximum crystal voltage falls off rapidly above 1 MHz. This maximum voltage curve is a useful design tool.

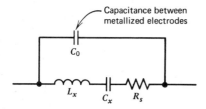

Figure 2.2. Equivalent circuit for a quartz crystal near fundamental resonance.

TABLE 2.1
Some Measured Quartz Crystal Parameters

Frequency	L_x (H)	C_x (pF)	R_s (Ω)	C_0 (pF)
4 kHz	—	—	45,000	15.
50 kHz	—	—	20,000	9.
100 kHz	52.	0.049	400	8.
1 MHz	4.2	0.0060	240	3.4
10 MHz	0.0098	0.026	5	8.5
20 MHz (3d harmonic)	0.053	0.0012	—	5.6
50 MHz (3d harmonic)	—	—	—	4.2
100 MHz (5th harmonic)	—	—	—	5.7

Since crystals frequently operate slightly off resonance, measuring the voltage across the crystal is meaningless as a measure of current through the crystal. The practical solution is to measure the current through the crystal by means of the voltage drop across a series element and calculate the crystal's power dissipation by $I^2 R_s$, where I is the current through the crystal and R_s is the crystal's internal series resistance.

At frequencies above about 2 MHz, the AC voltage swing from an

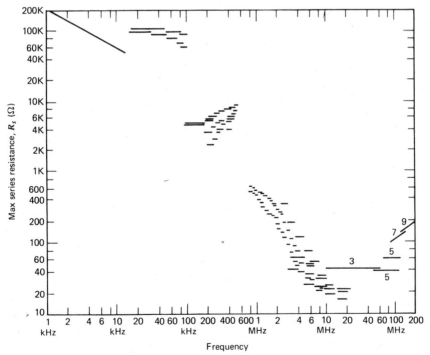

Figure 2.3. Maximum crystal series resistance R_s as a function of frequency.

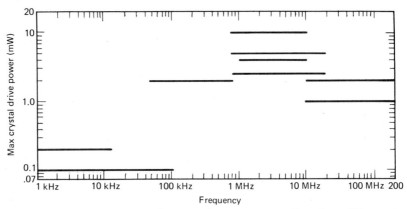

Figure 2.4. Maximum crystal power dissipation as a function of frequency.

oscillator circuit operating from a 5 V power supply can be higher than what should be put across the crystal at series resonance. An amplitude-limiting scheme is frequently needed to take care of this problem.

There is no difference in the construction of a *series-resonant* crystal and a *parallel-resonant* crystal, which are manufactured exactly alike. The only difference between them is that the series-resonant frequency of the parallel-resonant crystal is set 100 ppm or so lower than the desired operating frequency. Parallel resonance means that a small capacitance of 32 pF or so should be placed across crystal terminals to obtain the desired operating frequency. This presumes that the external load across the crystal's terminals has a high impedance. If the external load across the crystal's terminals has a low impedance, then parallel resonance means that a small capacitance of 32 pF or so should be placed

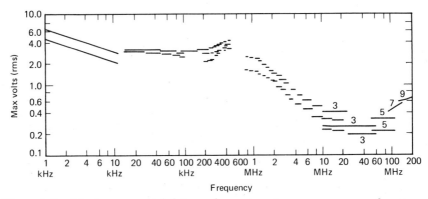

Figure 2.5. Maximum crystal-drive voltage at series resonance as a function of frequency.

in series with the crystal and its low-impedance load to obtain the desired operating frequency.

Putting an external capacitor in series with the crystal's internal motional capacitance C_x reduces the net total series capacitance of the two and thereby raises the crystal's series-resonant frequency. In practice, specifying parallel resonance simply tells the manufacturer to set the crystal's series resonance a little lower than the frequency requested by the user, so that when the crystal is put in series with (or parallel with) a small capacitor, the crystal's resonant frequency will be what the user wants.

The AT cut offers a lot of advantages over other crystal cuts and has been brought to a high state of perfection. Warner and others at Bell Telephone Laboratories developed two outstanding AT crystal designs at 2.5 and 5 MHz for use in high-performance frequency standards. Both operate on the fifth harmonic. The 2.5-MHz crystal uses a large quartz blank 30 mm in diameter. Several papers published by the group at Bell Labs on crystal designs and the oscillator circuits used with them are listed in the reference and bibliography sections in this book.

Among many items of interest, Warner [11, 12] and Bömmel et al. [13, 14] reported the following on AT crystals:

1. Crystals operate differently in a vacuum than in air.
2. The series resistance of a crystal is 3 times lower in vacuum than in air, with a corresponding improvement in Q. Above 30 MHz, there is no measurable difference in Q between operations in air or vacuum.
3. The maximum attainable crystal Q is an inverse function of frequency. It is also a function of the diameter and surface curvature of the crystal blank.
4. Harmonic operation gives improved Q when the crystal is operated in air. In a vacuum, the crystal's Q is the same for either fundamental or harmonic operation.
5. A glass container for the crystal gives less long-term frequency drift than a metal container.

The internal series resistance of the large high-Q 2.5-MHz crystal was 65 Ω. Since this varies as the cube of the harmonic, the crystal's internal resistance would be $1/27$ of 65 or 2.4 Ω, if it were operated in a fundamental mode at 2.5 MHz. A value of 2.4 Ω is too low a load resistance for a transistor amplifier stage to drive easily. Warner [11] points out that this is one of the main reasons for operating a high-Q crystal at a harmonic frequency—the crystal's internal series resistance is higher and much easier for a transistor amplifier stage to drive.

If we want to electrically pull a crystal off frequency with a variable capacitance diode or other means, it should be done at the crystal's fundamental frequency. The crystal will be much harder to pull off frequency and will not pull so far (percentagewise) when operated at a harmonic frequency, because of the crystal's greater phase shift with a given change in frequency.

CHAPTER THREE

FUNDAMENTALS OF CRYSTAL OSCILLATION

3.1. OSCILLATION

A circuit will oscillate if it has positive feedback and a loop gain greater than 1. With a crystal as a series element in the loop and no other frequency-sensitive elements in the circuit, it will oscillate at the crystal's fundamental series-resonant frequency. A quartz crystal always wants to oscillate at its fundamental frequency and must be forced to oscillate at a harmonic.

When the oscillator circuit's feedback loop is first closed, sine wave oscillation begins, and the amplitude increases until overload occurs. The waveform at overload becomes a clipped sine wave and finally approaches a square wave at heavy overload. Crystal oscillators can usually provide either a square wave or a sine wave output. The signal driving the crystal is most often a square wave, and the signal out of the crystal is always a sine wave. Either waveform can be used for an output by tapping the appropriate point in the circuit.

3.2. SERIES RESONANCE VERSUS PARALLEL RESONANCE

There is no such thing as a parallel-resonant crystal oscillator. All crystal oscillators operate either at or near (above or below) series resonance. What is usually meant by parallel resonance is that the crystal has a high load impedance across its terminals. This is in contrast to series resonance, which usually means that the crystal has a low load impedance across its terminals. Series resonance *physically exists* in the crystal, but

9

parallel resonance exists only as a crystal *measurement* phenomenon. When the impedance of a crystal is measured externally as a function of frequency, an impedance peak will be found above series resonance, where part of the crystal's motional inductance L_x parallel resonates with the crystal's shunt terminal capacitance C_0.

From a circuit viewpoint, the crystal's shunt terminal capacitance C_0 should be considered as part of the external load on the crystal and not as part of its internal frequency-controlling L_x and C_x elements. Experimental data confirming this viewpoint are given later. When parallel resonance is mentioned in this book, it will have the usual meaning that the crystal has a high load impedance across its terminals, and not that the crystal is oscillating at the higher frequency where the crystal's input impedance peak occurs.

3.3 BASIC CRYSTAL CIRCUIT CONNECTIONS

How should a quartz crystal be connected in an oscillator circuit? What load impedance should it see? These are key questions in the design of an oscillator circuit. For a crystal to control the frequency of an oscillator circuit, the crystal must maximize the oscillator's gain at the oscillation frequency and minimize it at all other frequencies. It is well-known that a crystal's impedance goes to a minimum at series resonance and to a maximum at parallel resonance. The design question is how best to take advantage of this and give the crystal maximum control of the oscillation frequency.

One approach is to connect the crystal as a series element in the oscillator circuit, as shown in Fig. 3.1. The crystal acts as part of a voltage divider with the resistor R_{load} and operates at series resonance with zero phase shift through the voltage divider. The gain $|E_0/E_i|$ through the

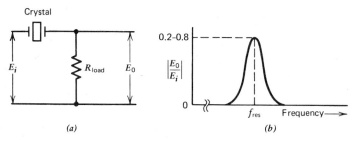

Figure 3.1. Typical crystal series connection: (*a*) circuit and (*b*) circuit gain versus frequency.

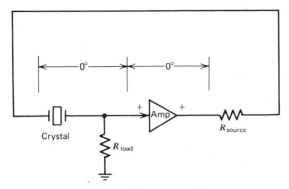

Figure 3.2. Typical series oscillator circuit.

voltage divider reaches a maximum of something less than 1.0 at series resonance, as shown in Fig. 3.1.

Figure 3.2 shows a typical oscillator circuit using the crystal as a series element. To give the crystal maximum control of the loop gain, the crystal must have maximum control of the voltage divider, which means that both the source and load resistances shown in Fig. 3.2 should be small with respect to the crystal's impedance at series resonance; that is, they should be smaller than the internal series resistance R_s of the crystal.

An alternative way of looking at the series circuit in Fig. 3.2 is that the amplifier's output puts a voltage across the crystal, and the amplifier's input samples the current through the crystal, which is a maximum at series resonance. Again, the crystal will have maximum control of the loop gain when both R_{source} and R_{load} are small with respect to the crystal's internal series resistance R_s.

Another design approach is to connect the crystal as a shunt element, as shown in Fig. 3.3. The crystal is again part of a voltage divider. Here, the voltage divider's series element has to be a capacitor or inductor and *cannot* be a resistor. Figure 3.3 shows a capacitor C_1 as the series element of the voltage divider. Putting the capacitor C_1 in series with the crystal raises the oscillation frequency slightly above the crystal's series-resonance frequency. The voltage divider's gain $|E_0/E_i|$ at the oscillation frequency peaks at about 10–15X, as shown in Fig. 3.3, because the circuit resonates at this frequency. There is a 90° phase lead through the voltage divider at the oscillation frequency at the peak of the gain curve. To use this shunt network in an oscillator circuit requires adding another 90° phase-lead (or lag) network into the circuit.

Figure 3.4 shows a shunt oscillator circuit with a 90° phase-lead network, using the inductor L and the amplifier's output resistance R_{source} to provide the phase lead. This is the Miller circuit.

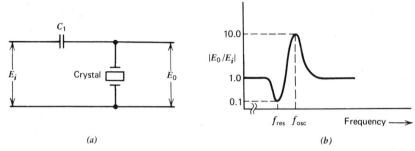

Figure 3.3. Typical crystal shunt connection: (*a*) circuit and (*b*) circuit gain versus frequency.

Figure 3.5 shows a shunt oscillator circuit with a 90° phase-lag network, using a shunt capacitor C_2 and the amplifier's output resistance R_{source} to provide the phase lag. This is the Colpitts circuit. Note that the phase-lead network requires using an inverting amplifier, while the phase-lag network requires a noninverting amplifier. The crystal's load resistance R_{load} must be high in both Figs. 3.4 and 3.5 to give the crystal maximum control of the voltage divider's gain.

In actual practice, the phase-lead and lag networks used in shunt circuits generate a little less than 90° of phase shift. This does not matter because the circuit's oscillation frequency will simply move slightly off the amplitude peak shown in Fig. 3.3, changing the phase shift through the voltage divider enough to compensate for the less-than-90° phase shift of the lead and lag networks.

The need for low load and source resistances on the crystal for series operation and a high load resistance on the crystal for shunt operation is typical of crystal oscillator circuits. How low and how high these resistances should be to give good in-circuit Q is an important design

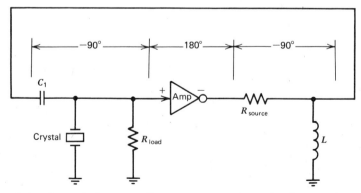

Figure 3.4. Typical shunt oscillator circuit, with 90° lead network (Miller).

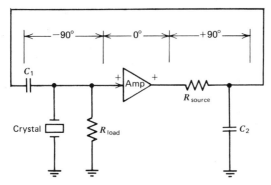

Figure 3.5. Typical shunt oscillator circuit, with 90° lag network (Colpitts).

parameter that affects the circuits' short-term frequency stability. This subject is discussed in detail in Sections 4.2, 6.1, and 6.2.

3.4. CRYSTAL RESPONSE TO A STEP INPUT

What happens to a crystal when it is driven by a square wave? Most series-resonant oscillator circuits put a square wave of voltage across the crystal and sample the current through the crystal by means of a resistor in series with it. The current signal is then fed into the amplifier input. The relationship between the voltage across the crystal and the current through it is important for understanding how the series-resonant oscillator circuit works. This can be understood by first looking at how the crystal responds to a step input and then extending this to a periodically reversing step input; that is, a square wave.

A simplified equivalent circuit for the crystal at its fundamental series resonance is the series RLC network, as shown in Fig. 3.6a. The crystal's shunt terminal capacitance C_0 is ignored here. A current-sampling resistor R_{ext} is added in series with the crystal, and the crystal is driven by a step input of voltage E_i. For simplicity, the two series resistors R_s and R_{ext} are combined into one R. The relationship between the applied voltage and resulting crystal current is given by the Laplace transform,

$$\overline{G}(s) = \frac{\overline{e}_i(s)}{\overline{i}(s)} = \frac{Ls^2 + Rs + 1/C}{s}$$

For a voltage step input,

$$\overline{e}_i(s) = \frac{1}{s}$$

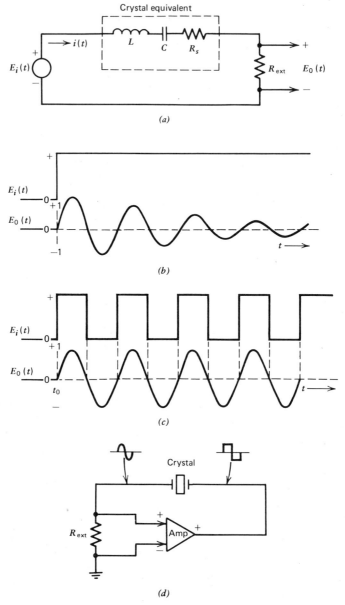

Figure 3.6. Crystal response to a square wave drive.

14

Using the inverse transform, the transient solution for the output voltage across R_{ext} is

$$E_0\,(t) = i\,(t)\,R_{ext} = \frac{R_{ext}e^{-t/(2RL)}\,\sin\,[\sqrt{C/L - 1/(4R^2L^2)}\;t]}{\sqrt{C/L - 1/(4R^2L^2)}}$$

The significance of this equation is that the current through the crystal is a (damped) sine wave and phased so that its starting point at the 0° phase-angle position is time coincident with the start of the step input, as shown in Fig. 3.6b. If the step input is reversed (i.e., dropped back to zero) every time the current sine wave goes to zero at 180° and 360°, the exponential decay term drops out, and the transient solution becomes the steady-state solution. The phase relationship between the input square wave of voltage and the output sine wave of current then becomes as shown in Fig. 3.6c. Note that there is no phase shift between them.

If the sine wave of crystal current is fed into an amplifier with enough gain so that the amplifier output saturates and makes a square wave out of the sine wave and if this square wave is used to drive the crystal as shown in Fig. 3.6d, then conditions for a periodically reversed step input are obtained, and there is continuous oscillation in the crystal. If the crystal and its amplifier circuit are actually built as shown in Fig. 3.6d, the sine and square wave waveforms observed will be seen to have the same polarity and phasing as shown in Fig. 3.6c. This concept of zero phase shift between the crystal's square wave input and its sine wave output underlies the operation of the series-resonant oscillator circuit.

CHAPTER FOUR

CIRCUIT DESIGN CHARACTERISTICS

The most important parameters in designing a crystal oscillator circuit are:

1. Crystal's internal series resistance R_s.
2. Load impedance across the crystal terminals.
3. Oscillator's loop gain.
4. Reduced crystal voltage limits above 1 MHz.
5. DC biasing of the transistor and IC amplifier stages.
6. Transistor's high-frequency gain limit f_T.

Note that three of the six circuit design parameters are crystal related. Each of these parameters is discussed in the following sections.

4.1. CRYSTAL'S INTERNAL SERIES RESISTANCE R_s

The design of an oscillator circuit is overwhelmingly dominated by the crystal's internal series resistance R_s—far more than by any other parameter. A crystal's series resistance R_s varies from a low of 10 Ω at 20 MHz to 200,000 Ω at 1 kHz. The problem comes in providing the wide range in load resistance required to match the wide range in the crystal's series resistance R_s. For series resonance, the crystal's load resistance is usually set equal to or somewhat less than the crystal's internal series resistance R_s, in order to get good in-circuit Q. For parallel resonance, the

17

load resistance has to be much higher, up to 500 MΩ at 1 kHz, to get good in-circuit Q.

Considerable variation in circuit design is required to provide such a wide variation in the crystal's load resistance. At high frequencies, emitter follower outputs will provide low-resistance sources and loads. At medium frequencies, transistor bases and collectors, FET source follower outputs, and FET drains will all provide medium-resistance sources and loads. And at low frequencies, FET gates will provide high-resistance loads. The gain of a FET amplifier stage is about an order of magnitude less than that of a bipolar transistor stage, so that a second amplifier stage is usually required whenever a FET is used.

4.2. LOAD IMPEDANCE ACROSS THE CRYSTAL TERMINALS

The external load tied across the crystal terminals has a considerable effect on the crystal's frequency and its frequency stability. The oscillation current through the crystal's internal frequency-controlling elements L_x and C_x passes out of and back into the crystal through the crystal terminals. The crystal is driven by putting a voltage source in series with this current loop. The resulting current through the crystal's frequency-controlling elements is measured by sampling the voltage drop across a series element in the loop.

Ignoring the crystal's shunt terminal capacitance C_0, putting an inductor or capacitor in series with the crystal's terminals will put the inductor or capacitor in series with the current flowing through the crystal's internal frequency-controlling elements $L_x C_x$. This changes the total net series inductance or capacitance in the current loop and the loop's resonant frequency. Putting a small variable capacitor in series in this loop is a common method of trimming oscillator frequency. Whether or not the crystal's shunt terminal capacitance C_0 can be ignored depends, of course, on the relative impedance of the series inductor or capacitor with respect to the impedance of C_0.

If a low-impedance load is used across the crystal terminals, the circuit is called series resonant. This low impedance has to include the complete external circuit impedance seen by the crystal, looking at the circuit from the crystal terminals. This includes the output resistance of the drive amplifier, the current-sampling load resistor, and the input resistance of the amplifier's input.

If a high load impedance is used across the crystal terminals, the circuit is called parallel resonant. The crystal has a shunt terminal capacitance C_0 of its own, amounting to 3–15 pF. This shunt terminal capacitance C_0 is part of the external load on the crystal as far as the crystal's internal frequency-controlling elements L_x and C_x are concerned. The impedance of C_0 normally defines the highest load impedance that can be put across the crystal terminals, although at high frequencies (above 50–70 MHz), it is parallel resonated with an inductor to remove it from the circuit.

Tying a resistive load R_{load} across the crystal terminals gives a total paralleled RC load of R_{load} and C_0 across the crystal's frequency-controlling elements $L_x C_x$. To determine loading effects on the crystal, it is convenient to convert this paralleled RC load combination to its equivalent series values of R_{series} and C_{series}. The load the crystal wants to see is the smallest possible equivalent series load resistance R_{series}, since this resistance reduces both the in-circuit Q and short-term frequency stability. In practice, if good oscillator performance is to be obtained, the equivalent series load resistance R_{series} should be made equal to or somewhat less than the crystal's internal series resistance R_s.

The equivalent series load capacitance C_{series} is in series with the crystal's frequency-determining motional capacitance. Like any two capacitors in series, the effect of C_{series} is to reduce the net series capacitance in the crystal circuit and raise the resonant frequency. Besides raising the resonant frequency, the crystal itself does not seem to care about this external series capacitance. If the equivalent series load is inductive rather than capacitive, the inductance is in series with the crystal's frequency-determining motional inductance. And as is the case with any two inductors in series, the total net series inductance is raised, which lowers the resonant frequency accordingly.

In a series-resonant circuit such as shown in Fig. 3.2, the crystal with its internal series resistance R_s acts as a voltage divider with the load resistance R_L. A tradeoff must be made here between maximum in-circuit Q and a minimum gain loss. If the load resistance R_L is made very small for better Q, then a large gain loss is introduced by the voltage divider, which has to be compensated for by a larger amplifier gain. A good compromise is to make the load resistance R_L equal to one-half the crystal's internal series resistance R_s, and the source resistance R_{source} equal to or somewhat less than one-half the crystal's series resistance R_s. Then, the crystal's internal Q, which is limited by its internal series resistance R_s, is only degraded in the circuit by a factor of 2 to 1. The gain loss through the crystal's voltage divider network is then only 4 to 1.

4.3. OSCILLATOR LOOP GAIN

A crystal oscillator does not need much loop gain. Overall loop gain values of 2–10X are sufficient, and a gain of 4–5X is about optimum. The

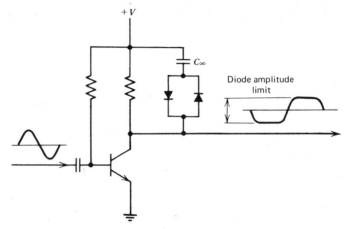

Figure 4.1. Diode amplitude clamp.

crystal and the network surrounding it usually have a gain loss of 1.5–
50X, so the amplifier used has to provide a gain of 3–200X. With only a
few exceptions, one or two transistors will provide more than enough
gain for any oscillator circuit. A single transistor stage can provide a
maximum gain of about 70X, so many oscillator circuits use only one
transistor. The network around the crystal is frequently adjusted to keep
its losses within the gain limits of a single transistor stage.

4.4. REDUCED CRYSTAL VOLTAGE LIMITS ABOVE 1 MHz

Because of the crystal's dissipation limit, there is a maximum operating
voltage that can be put across the crystal. This maximum operating voltage varies with frequency. Figure 2.5 is a graph of the maximum voltage
that can be put across a crystal of any frequency at its series resonance.
Assuming the usual square wave drive, a crystal-drive amplitude of 2
Vrms or 4 Vp-p can be used at all frequencies below 1 MHz. Figure 2.5
shows that from 1 to 20 MHz the maximum crystal-drive level drops from
4 Vp-p down to about 0.3 Vrms or 0.6 Vp-p and remains at that level to
100 MHz. From 100 to 200 MHz, maximum crystal-drive voltage rises
again to about 1.2 Vp-p at 200 MHz.

   With a 5 V power supply, about 4 Vp-p is the normal circuit signal
level expected with saturated transistor operation. What this means is
that in order to use a 5 V power supply at frequencies above 1 MHz,
some sort of voltage limiter must be used to minimize crystal heating and
prevent excessive frequency drift. With discrete transistor circuits, the

voltage swing at the collector can be limited to almost any level by adjusting the transistor's emitter resistor. Another possibility is to use ECL circuitry, where the voltage swing is limited to 0.8 Vp-p.

Amplitude-limiting schemes can be rather elaborate. A simple and effective approach is Harrison's method [15] of using two paralleled diodes in series with a capacitor (for DC voltage isolation), as shown in Fig. 4.1. Two signal diodes such as the 1N4148 will clamp the amplitude at 1.2 Vp-p. Two Schottky diodes such as the 1N5711 will clamp at 0.8 Vp-p. Both clamping levels are useful in practice.

The maximum crystal voltage curve given in Fig. 2.5 is a power dissipation limit and applies at exact series resonance only. If the crystal is operated off series resonance, then the applied voltage can be increased. Moving the crystal off series resonance by 4 ppm will increase the crystal's impedance to about four times its series resistance value and will quadruple the voltage that can be applied without exceeding the crystal's dissipation limit. In most oscillator circuits, the frequency is adjustable, so that it is difficult to tell beforehand whether the crystal will be operating at series resonance or not. The conservative approach is to set the voltage amplitude at a safe level for operation at exact series resonance. One unfortunate fallout of the crystal's low voltage limit at high frequencies is that an amplifier stage is frequently required at the oscillator's output to boost up the oscillator's low signal level to a usable logic level.

4.5. DC BIASING OF TRANSISTOR AND IC AMPLIFIER STAGES

If a transistor or IC is not biased to an operating point within its linear region when power is applied, oscillation will not start. Proper biasing is the key to solving the no-start problem that plagues some oscillators. Biasing is discussed in detail in Chapter 9.

4.6. TRANSISTOR HIGH-FREQUENCY GAIN LIMIT f_T

Starting at some frequency in the 1–100 MHz range, the gain of a bipolar transistor falls off with increasing frequency at approximately 6 dB/octave, due to the RC roll-off of the intrinsic resistance of the transistor's base material and the base-to-emitter's junction capacitance. On the transistor data sheets, this is specified by the frequency f_T, where the transistor's current gain has dropped down to 1, and no amplification can

TABLE 4.1
Some Useful High-Frequency Transistors for Oscillator Circuits

Transistor	h_{FE} Minimum (@I_c, mA)	I_c Average (max, mA)	f_T Minimum (MHz)	C_{cb} Maximum (pF)	t_{on}, t_{off} (max nsec)	$R_b C_c$ Maximum (psec)	V_{CEO} Maximum (V)
npn							
2N2369A	40 @ 10 20 @ 100	200	500	4.0 (output to base)	12, 18	—	15
2N3509	100 @ 10 30 @ 100	—	—	4.0	12, 18	—	20
2N3694	100 @ 10	200	200	3.5 (output to base)	—	—	45
2N4265	100 @ 10	200	300	4.0	25, 35	—	12
2N5179	25 @ 3	50	900	1.0	—	14	12
MPS6595	25 @ 10 20 @ 50	—	1200	1.3	3.3,3.6 (typ)	9 (typical)	12
MRF517	40 @ 60	150	2200	4.5 (output to base)	—	—	25
MRF525[a]	60 @ 80	150	2200	4.0 (output to base)	—	—	25
MRF904	30 @ 5	30	4000 typical	1.0	—	—	15
MRF905	20 @ 100	150	2500 typical	5.0 (output to base)	—	—	20
MRF914	30 @ 20	40	4500 typical	1.0	—	—	12
pnp							
2N4208	30 @ 10	100	700	3.0 (output to base)	15, 20	—	12
2N4258A	30 @ 10	100	700	3.0 (output to base)	15, 18	—	12
2N4957	20 @ 2	30	1200	0.8	—	8	30
2N5583	20 @ 40	500	1000	5.0	—	11 (typical)	30
MM4049	20 @ 25	30	4000	1.3	—	15	10

[a]Case tied to emitter.

TABLE 4.2
Some Useful N-channel JFETs for Oscillator Circuits

JFET	BV_{gss} (V)	I_{DSS} Minimum (mA)	$g_{fs}{}^{b}$ Minimum (μmho)	C_{gd} Maximum (pF)	C_{gs} Maximum (pF)
2N4416A	35	5	4,500	0.8 (rss)	4. (iss)
J309	25	12	10,000	2.5	5.
U309[c]	25	12	10,000[c]	2.5	5.

[a] Case tied to gate terminal; designed for grounded gate operation.
[b] g_{fs}, common source transconductance.
[c] g_{fg}, common gate transconductance.

23

occur. If a transistor has a DC current gain of 100 and f_T of 200 MHz, then 2 MHz is the highest frequency at which the full current gain is available. To make an oscillator at 10 MHz, we need a transistor with a f_T of 1000 MHz to get a current gain of 100 at 10 MHz; however, in manufacturers' catalogs, the selection of transistors with f_T's of 1000 MHz or higher is pretty thin. Table 4.1 lists some useful high-frequency transistors for oscillator circuits.

In contrast to the bipolar transistor, the transconductance (or gain) of a FET is constant up to about 1000 MHz. At frequencies of 10–100 MHz, such FET characteristics as high transconductance, minimum input capacitance, and minimum feedback capacitance (Miller effect) are the important ones. Table 4.2 lists some useful high-frequency FETs for oscillator circuits.

CHAPTER FIVE

BASIC OSCILLATOR CIRCUITS

This chapter describes the basic design of different oscillator circuits and how they work. To give the reader a better overall view, a short summary describing each circuit is given first. This preliminary overview is followed by a more detailed description of each circuit. The so-called parallel-resonant (high load impedance) circuits are covered first, followed by series-resonant (low load impedance) types, and VHF harmonic circuits are described last. For simplicity and to avoid obscuring the oscillator concepts, the transistor biasing networks are shown in simplified form only. The actual biasing networks can be seen in the actual circuit schematics in Chapters 10 and 11.

5.1. BRIEF OVERVIEW AND CIRCUIT SURVEY

This section gives a brief overview of all the oscillator circuits. Circuit schematics of the oscillators are shown in Figs. 5.1–5.4. Parallel-resonant circuits are shown in Figs. 5.1a–d, series-resonant circuits in Figs. 5.2a–d and 5.3a–c, and harmonic circuits in Figs. 5.4a and b. Figure captions give a brief summary of each circuit's performance. Many of these circuits have a limited frequency range due to the wide variation in load resistance that the crystal needs to see over the frequency range of 1 kHz–200 MHz.

Figure 5.5 shows two circuits not covered in detail because they have little to offer. The first is the transformer-coupled circuit in Fig. 5.5a. The transformer provides a 180° phase reversal and allows series-

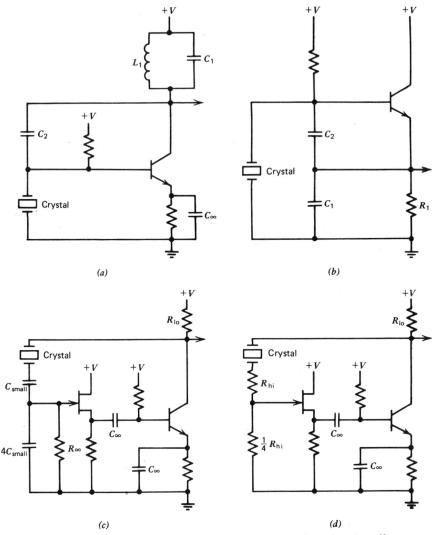

Figure 5.1. Parallel-resonant circuits (high load impedance): (*a*) Miller—poor circuit; poor frequency stability. (*b*) Colpitts—good circuit; fair frequency stability. Circuit is far more complex than it appears to be; widely used. (*c*) Low capacitance load—works reasonably well; fair frequency stability. (*d*) High resistance load—works reasonably well; poor frequency stability.

resonant operation with one transistor instead of two. This had some value in the vacuum tube era, but, today, it is more practical to use a second transistor to provide the 180° phase reversal.

The second circuit not covered in detail is the capacitance-bridge circuit in Fig. 5.5*b*. This circuit cancels out the crystal's terminal shunt capacitance C_0, but the cancellation can be done in a simpler fashion by shunting the crystal with an inductance and tuning it to parallel reso-

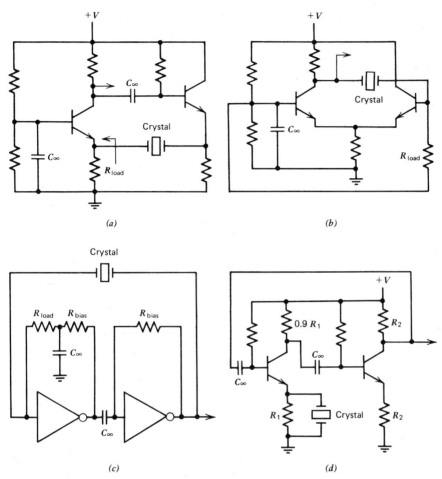

Figure 5.2. Series-resonant circuits (low load impedance): (*a*) Common base—works very well; good circuit; good frequency stability. (*b*) Common base, low frequency—works very well; good circuit. Provides high crystal load resistance needed at low frequencies; good frequency stability. (*c*) Two-inverters-IC—works fairly well; fair frequency stability. With TTL, oscillates spuriously when crystal is removed; widely used. (*d*) Emitter coupled—works fairly well; good frequency stability.

nance with C_0. Two variations of the C_0 capacitance-bridge cancellation idea at 100 MHz are included in the test circuits, however (see Sections 10.19 and 10.24).

5.2. MILLER

The Miller is a parallel-resonant circuit, and a basic schematic is shown in Fig. 5.6*a*. The crystal is used as a shunt impedance element to ground.

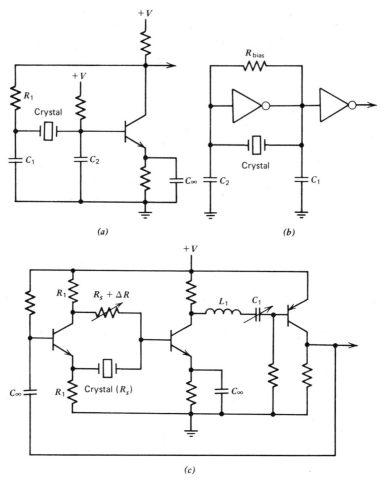

Figure 5.3. More series-resonant circuits (low load impedance): (*a*) Pierce—very close to series resonance. One of the best circuits; very good frequency stability, best overall design; widely used. (*b*) Pierce-IC—close to series resonance. Good circuit; good frequency stability; widely used. (*c*) Modified Meacham—one of the best circuits; best short-term frequency stability. Complex circuit, difficult to design.

The voltage across the crystal is amplified and inverted by the transistor and fed back to the crystal through a small capacitance C_2. The collector tank circuit $L_1 C_1$ is tuned to a frequency above resonance, so that the net impedance of $L_1 C_1$ is inductive at the frequency of oscillation. The tank circuit $L_1 C_1$ must be inductive at the frequency of oscillation, or the circuit will not oscillate. C_1 is not necessary for the circuit to oscillate, but it cleans up the waveform across L_1 considerably, which is absolutely awful without the capacitor across it.

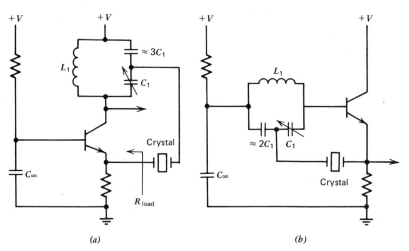

(a)   (b)

Figure 5.4. VHF harmonic circuits (20–200 MHz): (*a*) Butler common base—operates at or near series resonance; fair to poor circuit design. Has parasitics, touchy to tune; fair frequency stability. (*b*) Butler emitter follower—operates at or near series resonance; very good circuit design. No parasitics, easy to tune, low impedance output; good frequency stability.

The circuit operates as follows. The transistor provides a 180° phase reversal. The tank circuit L_1C_1 is inductive at the oscillation frequency, and together with the collector's output resistance provides a nominal 90° phase lead. And C_2, together with the crystal operating above resonance as an inductance, provides 90° more phase lead, so that the total phase shift around the loop is zero.

This is not a good oscillator circuit because the waveforms across the crystal are very poor and the frequency is unstable. It turns out that the

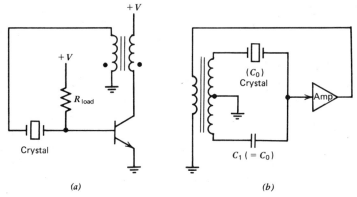

(a)   (b)

Figure 5.5. Two oscillator circuits not covered in detail: (*a*) transformer coupled and (*b*) capacitance bridge.

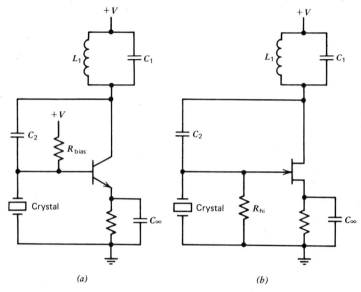

Figure 5.6. Miller circuit: (a) transistor version and (b) FET version.

frequency of oscillation is quite sensitive to the value of the series feed-back capacitor C_2, which is about 5–40 pF. Because of the Miller effect, the effective value of C_2 consists of the actual capacitor C_2 shown in Fig. 5.6a plus the transistor's internal base-to-collector capacitance, both multiplied by the transistor's voltage gain. The gain changes with temperature, power supply voltage, and from transistor to transistor. This means that the effective value of C_2 is not stable, and as a result, neither is the frequency of oscillation.

The transistor version of the Miller circuit will operate at high or medium frequencies, but not at low frequencies. At low frequencies, the resistive loading of the transistor's base input resistance across the high-impedance crystal is so great that the crystal will not oscillate.

The FET version of the Miller circuit is shown in Fig. 5.6b and can be used at any frequency: low, medium, or high. The crystal voltage waveform is much better with a FET than with a transistor. The frequency is still unstable and for the same reason: variability in the effective feedback capacitance C_2 due to changes in the FET's gain.

5.3. COLPITTS

The Colpitts is a parallel-resonant circuit, and a basic schematic is shown in Fig. 5.7a. Physically, the circuit is very simple, but analytically, it is

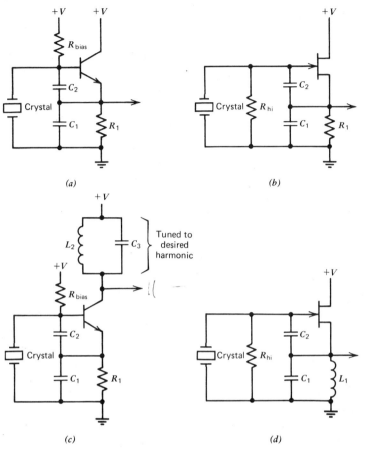

Figure 5.7. Colpitts circuit: (*a*) transistor version, (*b*) FET version, (*c*) frequency multiplier, and (*d*) harmonic (L_1C_1 is *not* tuned to resonance).

very complex. The oscillator has the following three distinct operating states.

The amplifier is an emitter follower with a gain of 1. The transistor conducts current over only a small portion of each oscillation cycle, usually about 15–20%. The transistor starts conducting a little before (about 10%) its base reaches the most positive peak of the sinusoid and stops conducting immediately after the positive peak. At the positive peak, the transistor saturates and clamps the crystal to the power supply bus through the forward-biased base-collector junction. Positive peak saturation lasts about 5–10% of an oscillation cycle. The transistor shuts off and remains nonconducting over the rest (80–85%) of the cycle. Thus, three circuit conditions exist during each cycle: a short interval (10%), with the transistor conducting properly and acting as an emitter follower;

a second short interval (5–10%), with the transistor saturated and shorting out the crystal; and a third long interval (80–85%), with the transistor shut off and nonconducting.

During the short state when the transistor is on and conducting normally, the circuit operates as follows. Referring to Fig. 5.7a, the crystal oscillates in a closed loop in series with C_2. C_2 is in series with the crystal's internal motional capacitance, which reduces the net capacitance in the crystal loop and raises the oscillation frequency. At this higher oscillation frequency, the crystal is inductive, and together with C_2, it generates a phase lead from the emitter to the base. C_1, together with the paralleled sum of R_1 and the emitter's output resistance R_{out}, generates an equal but opposite RC phase lag, giving zero total phase shift around the amplifier loop from emitter to base. Voltage gain from the emitter to the base is provided by partial series resonance between C_2 and the crystal's inductance.

During the long state when the transistor is shut off, the voltage across C_1 decays at a rate determined by the time constant $R_1 C_1$. The crystal's in-circuit Q is sensitive to the time constant $R_1 C_1$.

What values should be used for C_1, C_2, R_1, and R_{bias}? The answer is that they should be what the crystal wants them to be, which the crystal indicates by maximizing the voltage across itself. The biggest factor is external shunt resistance across the crystal terminals, which is such a strong factor that it determines the lowest frequency the circuit will oscillate at. This shunt resistance is the parallel sum of the biasing resistor R_{bias} and the transistor's input resistance. The transistor's input resistance is determined by the transistor's gain and the emitter's load resistance R_1. Using a high-gain transistor for the emitter follower helps considerably in raising shunt resistance across the crystal.

Not too surprisingly, there is a minimum crystal shunt resistance below which the crystal will not oscillate. This minimum shunt-resistance value varies directly with the crystal's internal series resistance R_s, which varies inversely with frequency. Table 5.1 lists two shunt-resistance values as a function of frequency: One is the shunt resistance at which the crystal's voltage amplitude drops 10%, and the other is the shunt-resistance value below which the circuit will not oscillate. These data were taken from several test circuits, so they are typical rather than exact.

As to the other component values in the Colpitts circuit, some change with frequency and some do not. In a transistor circuit, C_2 should be a fixed value of 40–70 pF, independent of oscillation frequency. The oscillation frequency is very sensitive to the value of C_2, but not to C_1. The

TABLE 5.1

Minimum Crystal Shunt Resistance in Colpitts Circuit

Frequency (MHz)	Shunt Resistance to Reduce Crystal Oscillation Amplitude by 10% (Ω)	Minimum Shunt Resistance for Oscillation to Occur (Ω)
0.004	220 meg	5 meg
0.05	10 meg	680K
0.1	3 meg	220K
0.2	470K	220K
0.5	330K	100K
1.	1 meg	22K
2.	470K	15K
5.	100K	4.7K
10.	100K	3.3K
20.	22K	2.2K

time constant $R_1 C_1$ should vary inversely with the oscillation frequency; that is,

$$R_1 C_1 \cong \frac{0.5}{f}$$

where R_1 is in ohms, C_1 is in μF, and f is in MHz. Additionally, there is no requirement for any specific ratio of C_1 to C_2.

Now, since the crystal's shunt resistance has to increase as the frequency drops, two requirements can be met at the same time in the transistor circuit by holding C_1 fixed and varying R_1 inversely with frequency. Increasing R_1 really helps raise the crystal's shunt resistance, because, in addition to increasing the input resistance of the emitter follower, it also raises the value of the biasing resistor R_{bias}. This technique of varying R_1 and holding C_1 fixed works very well in practice. The graph in Fig. 5.8 shows some typical values for R_1 and C_1 in the transistor-Colpitts circuit as a function of frequency.

The Colpitts circuit works better with a FET than a transistor. Figure 5.7b is a schematic of a Colpitts circuit using a FET. The main advantages are: (1) a better crystal waveform; (2) minimum oscillation frequency is lowered from 200 kHz (transistor) to 1 kHz (FET); (3) a higher crystal shunt resistance, which gives a higher in-circuit Q; and (4) no parasitic effects. The drawback to the FET is that above 10 MHz it does not work as well as the transistor circuit. This is because the output resistance of a FET source follower, which is 10 times higher than that of a

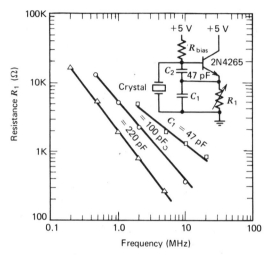

Figure 5.8. R_1 and C_1 values for Colpitts-transistor circuit.

transistor emitter follower, has a hard time driving the low load impedance that exists in the circuit at 10 MHz and above. With a FET, the waveform across the crystal is less distorted and more of a sine wave, as the waveform in Fig. 10.3a shows.

The minimum Colpitts oscillation frequency is lower with a FET than with a transistor, because the crystal's shunt-load resistance can be made higher with the FET. Table 5.1, for example, shows that at 4 kHz, a crystal shunt resistance of 220 MΩ will reduce voltage amplitude across the crystal by 10% and a shunt resistance lower than 5 MΩ will prevent oscillation. These are not practical values with a transistor circuit, but they are with a FET circuit.

In the FET version of the Colpitts oscillator shown in Fig. 5.7b, the value of the crystal's shunt resistance R_{hi} is picked from Table 5.1 as the value that will not decrease oscillation amplitude by more than 10%. C_2 should be a fixed value of 22–33 pF, independent of oscillation frequency (in the transistor circuit, C_2 should be a fixed value of 40–70 pF). The oscillation frequency is very sensitive to the value of C_2, but not to C_1. And like the transistor circuit, the time constant $R_1 C_1$ varies inversely with frequency:

$$R_1 C_1 \cong \frac{0.3}{f}$$

where R_1 is in ohms, C_1 is in μF, and f is in MHz.

To meet the inverse frequency requirement on the time constant $R_1 C_1$ in the FET-Colpitts circuit, it is convenient to hold R_1 constant at some convenient biasing value and vary C_1 with the frequency of oscillation.

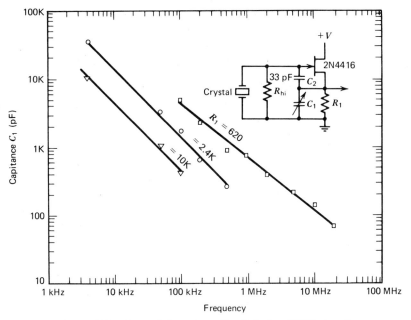

Figure 5.9. R_1 and C_1 values for Colpitts-FET circuit.

This is in contrast to the transistor-Colpitts circuit, where it was convenient to hold C_1 fixed and vary R_1. The graph in Fig. 5.9 shows some typical values of R_1 and C_1 as a function of frequency for the FET-Colpitts circuit. Additionally, there is no requirement for any specific ratio of C_1 to C_2.

In the transistor-Colpitts circuit, parasitics will occur at some nonoptimum circuit values. In contrast, no parasitics of any kind have been found in the FET-Colpitts circuit. The parasitics turn out to be third harmonic oscillations or a combination of fundamental and third harmonic oscillations. The circuit values are rather critical for obtaining this harmonic oscillation. The effect can be enhanced by decreasing the crystal's shunt resistance down to a point where the fundamental frequency is discouraged from oscillating while still keeping the shunt resistance high enough to permit oscillation at the third harmonic. Setting the time constant R_1C_1 for the third harmonic frequency also helps. Both third and fifth harmonic oscillation have been reported by Bahadur and Parshad [16]. The amplitude of oscillation obtained this way is rather low, and there is a better harmonic Colpitts circuit available, which is discussed in the following paragraphs.

The Colpitts can also be used as a harmonic multiplier and a harmonic oscillator, as shown in Figs. 5.7c and 5.7d. In Fig. 5.7c, an LC tank tuned to the desired harmonic is placed in the collector circuit, where it is isolated and has very little effect on what happens to the crystal at the transistor base. The crystal runs at its fundamental frequency, and the collector's L_2C_3 tank at a harmonic. The transistor conducts during only a short interval in each cycle (about 5–15% of the cycle period) at the crystal's fundamental frequency, which gives a short, sharp pulse of excitation once per fundamental cycle to the harmonically tuned tank in the collector circuit. The harmonic tank rings at its own natural frequency and is essentially resynchronized to the crystal's fundamental frequency once per fundamental cycle. This circuit has two drawbacks: The frequency is not constant from cycle to cycle, and the amplitude varies over the resynchronization interval.

In Fig. 5.7d, the crystal itself oscillates at the harmonic frequency. This circuit works much better than the circuit in Fig. 5.7c. Figure 5.7d shows a FET amplifier, but the circuit works equally well with a transistor. The only difference between this harmonic circuit and the fundamental circuit in Fig. 5.7b is that the resistor R_1 is replaced with the inductor L_1. The key to harmonic operation is to select L_1 so that its impedance at the harmonic oscillation frequency is equal to what R_1 in Fig. 5.7b should be to oscillate at that same frequency.

As an example, Fig. 5.10 shows a fundamental Colpitts circuit for 20 MHz. Figure 5.11 shows a third harmonic Colpitts circuit also for 20 MHz. Note that the impedance of the 10 μH inductor L_1 is approximately equal to R_1, 1200 Ω. The reason the circuit in Fig. 5.11 oscillates at the third harmonic (20 MHz) rather than at the fundamental (6.7 MHz) is that the impedance of L_1 should be 3600 Ω at 6.7 MHz for fundamental oscillation to occur, whereas the actual impedance of L_1 at 6.7 MHz is only 400 Ω or 1/9 of what it should be for fundamental oscillation.

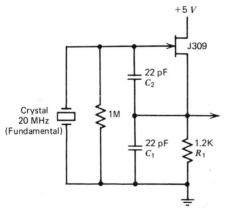

Figure 5.10. Fundamental Colpitts at 20 MHz.

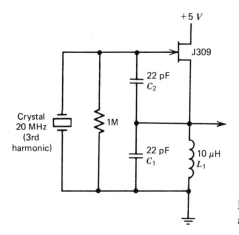

Figure 5.11. Third harmonic Colpitts at 20 MHz.

5.4. LOW CAPACITANCE LOAD

What happens when a low capacitance load (high impedance) is used on the crystal? The major effects are a higher oscillation frequency and a higher crystal output signal to the amplifier. The external load capacitance is in series with the crystal's internal motional capacitance, which reduces net oscillation capacitance and raises the resonant frequency proportionately. The output signal is larger because the impedance of the crystal's current measuring element is larger.

A basic schematic is shown in Fig. 5.12a. The crystal is driven by as low a source resistance as possible R_{lo}. The crystal's load consists of two small capacitors in series that act as a 5 to 1 voltage divider to isolate the amplifier's resistive loading and overload peak-clipping effects from the crystal. The amplifier's input stage is a FET in order to make the amplifier's input resistance as high as possible and minimize resistive-loading effects on the crystal.

The 5 to 1 capacitive voltage divider and, to a certain extent, using a FET input stage provide a linear input impedance to the crystal that will not overload and put a short circuit directly across the crystal over a part of the waveform cycle, as the Colpitts circuit does. The FET does overload as a gate-to-drain diode clamp to the power supply bus at the positive peak of the input waveform, but the 5 to 1 voltage divider hides it from the crystal.

Sampling the crystal current by means of the voltage across a capacitor in series with the crystal introduces a 90° phase lag in the amplifier loop. The amplifier itself provides a 180° phase inversion, and the two RC networks (R_1C_3 and $R_{lo}C_4$) in the amplifier introduce two additional 45° phase lags, for a total phase shift of 360° around the amplifier loop.

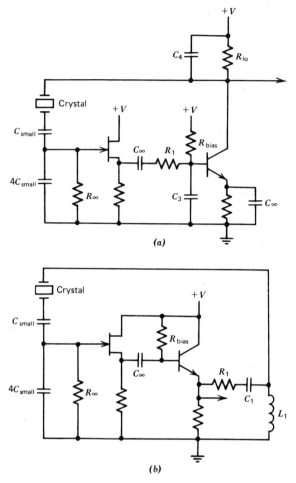

Figure 5.12. Low capacitance load circuit: (*a*) using an inverting amplifier, (*b*) using a noninverting amplifier.

The oscillator works equally well with a noninverting amplifier, as shown in Fig. 5.12*b*. The noninverting amplifier consists of a cascaded FET source follower and a transistor emitter follower, with a total amplifier gain of 0.7X. Additional gain is obtained by resonance effects between the inductive crystal and the series capacitors C_{small} and $4C_{small}$ and between L_1 and C_1. The 90° phase lag of the crystal's current-sampling capacitor $4C_{small}$ is compensated by the 90° phase lead of L_1, which is series resonant with C_1. The overall loop gain is controlled by two ratios: the ratio of the impedance of L_1 to R_1 and the ratio of the impedance of $4C_{small}$ to the impedance of L_1. L_1 is made relatively small and partially reduces the frequency increase caused by the low capacitance load C_{small} on the crystal.

5.5. HIGH RESISTANCE LOAD

What happens when a high resistance load is used on a crystal? Pretty much the same thing that happens when a low capacitance load is used. The major effects are a much higher oscillation frequency and a larger crystal output voltage to the amplifier. The higher oscillation frequency is due to the crystal's small terminal capacitance C_0 being in series with the crystal's internal motional capacitance, which reduces net oscillation capacitance and raises the resonant frequency.

A basic schematic is shown in Fig. 5.13. The circuit is very similar to the low capacitance load circuit in Fig. 5.12a except for the crystal loading. The crystal is driven by as low a resistance as possible, R_{lo}. The crystal's load consists of its terminal capacitance C_0 and two very large resistors (R_{hi} and $0.25\,R_{hi}$) that act as a 5 to 1 voltage divider to isolate the amplifier's overload peak-clipping effects from the crystal. The amplifier's input stage is a FET in order to make the amplifier's input resistance as high as possible and minimize crystal loading. The 5 to 1 voltage divider provides a linear impedance to the crystal that will not put a short circuit across the crystal over a part of the waveform cycle, as the Colpitts circuit does. The FET overloads as a gate-to-drain diode clamp at the positive peak of the input waveform, but the 5 to 1 voltage divider hides it from the crystal.

The input capacitance of the FET amplifier in Fig. 5.13 is 4 pF, which requires capacitive compensation C_3 of the resistive voltage divider. The reactive impedances of C_3 and the amplifier's 4-pF input capacitance at 1

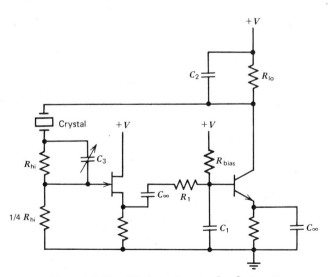

Figure 5.13. High resistance load circuit.

MHz are much lower than the resistance of the voltage divider, which means that the divider is really a capacitive divider rather than a resistive one. It also means a 90° phase lag, because the crystal's current is measured by the voltage drop across a capacitor rather than across a resistor.

The amplifier in Fig. 5.13 provides 180° phase inversion. The two RC networks (R_1C_1 and $R_{10}C_2$) introduce two additional 45° phase lags, for a total phase shift of 360° around the amplifier loop. The oscillator will work equally well with a noninverting amplifier, using a circuit similar to that shown in Fig. 5.12b but with a high-resistance voltage divider instead of the capacitive one shown in Fig. 5.12b.

5.6. COMMON BASE

The common base oscillator circuit is a series-resonant type, and a basic schematic is shown in Fig. 5.14a. This circuit has several good design characteristics: It uses a common base amplifier, which is unconditionally stable at all frequencies and has a very wide frequency response. An emitter follower reduces the amplifier's output resistance to a low value for driving the crystal. The crystal is tied between two emitters; one emitter acts as the crystal's load resistance and the other, as the crystal's source resistance. The emitter source and load resistances can be varied over a wide range to provide a suitable crystal load over a wide range of crystal resistances.

The basic circuit works well over a frequency range of 600 kHz–20 MHz. The frequency range can be extended to 4 kHz by moving the crystal to a different part of the circuit, as shown in Fig. 5.14c.

The common base circuit shows very clearly the strong effect that the crystal's internal series resistance R_s has on circuit design. Referring to Fig. 5.14a, we see that the net load resistance on the crystal is the parallel sum of R_2 and Q_1's emitter input resistance. The net load resistance and the crystal's internal series resistance R_s act as a voltage divider, which reduces loop gain. The lower the load resistance on the crystal, the more loop gain is reduced, and the larger the gain that Q_1 has to provide to maintain oscillation.

The gain of Q_1 is proportional to the ratio of its collector and emitter resistors R_1/R_2. So to keep the gain up, the emitter resistor R_2 should be kept small, and not allowed to get much bigger than Q_1's emitter input resistance. The emitter's input resistance is controlled by the emitter current, which can be varied over a wide range by varying the base bias voltage.

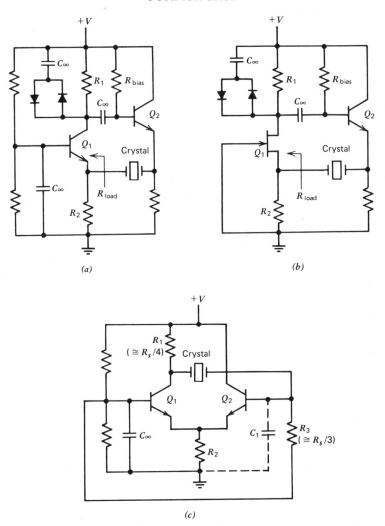

(a)

(b)

(c)

Figure 5.14. Common base and common gate oscillator circuits. The appropriate circuit is selected on the basis of the crystal's internal series resistance R_s. (a) At high frequencies: $5 < R_s < 400\ \Omega$; (b) At medium frequencies: $200 < R_s < 1200\ \Omega$; (c) At low frequencies: $1K < R_s < 100K\ \Omega$.

A transistor emitter's input resistance can be varied from 5 to 100 Ω, which is suited to the low resistance of crystals at high frequencies. At medium frequencies, replacing the transistor Q_1 with a FET will give the crystal a higher load resistance that is more appropriate to the medium resistance of crystals at these frequencies. Figure 5.14b shows a FET schematic that is appropriate for medium frequency use. The source input resistance for a high transconductance FET such as the

J309 (or U309) is about 200 Ω and for a medium transconductance FET such as the 2N4416, about 500 Ω. The crystal's load resistance can thus be varied from 200 to 500 Ω by selecting the FET used for Q_1.

It is important to note the diode amplitude clamp in Figs. 5.14a and 5.14b; the circuits do not work well without it. The purpose of the clamp is to limit oscillation amplitude and thereby keep both Q_1 and Q_2 operating in their linear regions over the complete waveform cycle. If either transistor saturates or ceases conduction at some point over the waveform cycle, the crystal's source and/or load resistances will switch suddenly to either a short circuit or a high value.

At low frequencies (i.e., below 600 kHz), crystals have a relatively high internal series resistance and need a high load resistance to avoid a large gain loss. To obtain this, the crystal is moved to a higher impedance part of the circuit, as shown in Fig. 5.14c. Here, the crystal is tied between collector and base. The two emitters are tied together and use a common emitter resistor. Q_2 should be a high-gain transistor in order to maximize both its base input resistance and the biasing resistor R_3 in parallel with the base of Q_2. Q_2 acts as an emitter follower driving Q_1 as a common base amplifier. The gain of Q_1 is controlled by the ratio of the collector and emitter resistors R_1/R_2. C_1 is a small noise-reducing capacitor, which eliminates extra noise switchings that occur at switching crossover points at these low frequencies.

At very low frequencies (below 4 kHz), where the crystal's internal series resistance R_s goes over 100K Ω, the circuit in Fig. 5.14c does not have enough gain to oscillate anymore because of the high gain loss through the crystal and its voltage divider. The circuit in Fig. 5.15 can then be used; it is not a common base amplifier circuit, but it is a series-resonant circuit. It uses a straightforward two-stage amplifier, with a FET for the input stage. There is more than enough gain available, so the crystal's source and load resistances R_1 and R_{load} can both be made considerably smaller than the crystal's internal series resistance R_s. This will give good in-circuit Q and good short-term frequency stability.

5.7. SERIES RESONANCE-IC

There are several ways integrated circuits can be used in a crystal oscillator. The two-inverter circuit shown in Fig. 5.16 is a popular one because of its simplicity and the ease of blending it into digital circuitry. The circuit is series resonant and uses two cascaded digital inverters for an amplifier. It can be built using CMOS-, TTL-, or ECL-type circuitry.

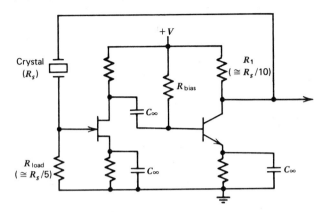

Figure 5.15. Alternative series-resonant circuit at very low frequencies, for $R_s >$ 50K Ω.

To solve the start-up problem, each inverter has a DC biasing resistor tied from its output to its input to bias the inverters halfway between the zero and one states, so that they will amplify when power is applied and the crystal will start oscillating. The two inverters are AC coupled to prevent the DC biasing loops on the two inverters from interfering with each other.

The biasing resistor on the first inverter is made up of two resistors in series, with the center point bypassed to ground through C_1. C_1 reduces the coupling of the switching signal from the output of the first inverter back into the crystal's output and helps clean up the crystal's output waveform. For good in-circuit Q and short-term frequency stability, R_{load} should be set equal to or somewhat less than the crystal's internal series resistance R_s.

The two-inverter circuit works well in CMOS and ECL, but in TTL, it has three drawbacks. First, the input resistance of a TTL inverter (or

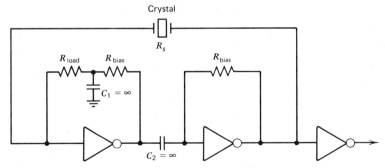

Figure 5.16. Series-resonant oscillator using ICs.

gate) goes low just before the instant of switching, creating a flat spot in the amplifier's input waveform at the worst possible time—during the switching interval. The flat spot makes the instant of switching more uncertain in time and worsens the oscillator's short-term stability. Second, the TTL version cannot be used above about 3 MHz because TTL voltage levels exceed the crystal's power dissipation limit. And third, the circuit will not oscillate below about 100 kHz because the parallel resistance of the first TTL inverter's input resistance and the biasing resistor R_{bias} act as a voltage divider with the crystal's internal series resistance R_s and attenuate loop gain too much.

Although Fig. 5.16 shows a crystal load resistor R_{load}, both R_{load} and capacitor C_1 are frequently omitted from the circuit, which reduces both the in-circuit Q and short-term frequency stability. Many computer circuits simply need a reliable clock with a 50-50 on/off ratio rather than the accuracy or stability provided by a quartz crystal. Therefore, omitting R_{load} and C_1 is not a loss under these conditions.

Another IC oscillator circuit is shown in Fig. 5.17. This is a series-resonant circuit that uses a voltage comparator or a line receiver for the amplifier.

5.8. PIERCE

The Pierce is a series-resonant circuit, and its schematic is shown in Fig. 5.18. The Pierce has many desirable characteristics. It will work at any frequency from the lowest to the highest—from 1 kHz–200 MHz. It has

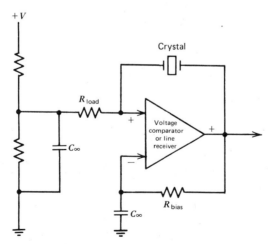

Figure 5.17. Another series-resonant IC oscillator.

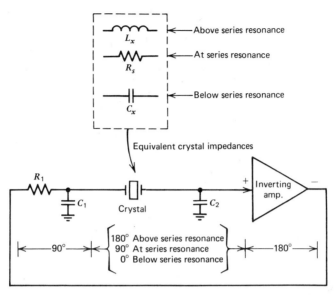

Figure 5.18. Pierce circuit, ideal operation.

very good short-term stability because the crystal's source and load impedances are mostly capacitive rather than resistive, which give it a high in-circuit Q. The circuit provides a large output signal and simultaneously drives the crystal at a low power level. The low power level in the crystal is very helpful at high frequencies, where crystals have low dissipation ratings.

Large phase shifts in RC networks and large shunt capacitances to ground on both sides of the crystal make the oscillation frequency relatively insensitive to small changes in the series resistances or shunt capacitances. In addition, RC roll-off networks and shunt capacitances to ground minimize any transient noise spikes, which give the circuit a high immunity to noise.

In most Pierce circuits, the amplifier consists of just one transistor, and it has no parasitic oscillations of any kind. Being a stable low-impedance circuit, it is not disturbed by connecting a scope probe to any circuit point. This makes it easy to see what is going on in the circuit.

The Pierce circuit does have one disadvantage. It needs a relatively high amplifier gain to compensate for relatively high gain losses in the circuitry surrounding the crystal.

Several writers in the literature, having noted that the Pierce and Colpitts have identical circuit layouts except for the location of the ground point, have used one set of mathematical equations to interpret both circuits. One set of equations can be applied to both circuits, but since the

two circuits operate differently, the equations must be interpreted differently in the two cases. The basic difference between the circuits is
that the crystal in the Pierce is designed to look into the lowest possible
impedance across its terminals, whereas the crystal in the Colpitts is designed to look into a high impedance across its terminals. This basic difference results in other differences. The operation of the Colpitts, which
is described in Section 5.3, is so different from that of the Pierce, described in this section, that there is little significance in using the same
set of equations to cover both circuits except that both are three-loop
networks containing the same number of RLC components.

To understand how the Pierce oscillator circuit works, the reader
should refer to Fig. 5.18. The total phase shift around the loop is 360°.
Idealistically speaking, the amplifier provides 180°, R_1C_1 acts as an integration network and provides a 90° phase lag, and the crystal, together
with C_2, acts as a second integration network and provides a second 90°
phase lag.

At series resonance, the crystal's impedance is a pure resistance, and
together with C_2, it acts like a RC integrating network, providing a 90°
phase lag, as shown in Fig. 5.18. Below series resonance, the crystal's
impedance is capacitive, as shown in Fig. 5.18, and together with C_2, it
acts like a capacitive voltage divider with 0° phase shift. Above series
resonance, the crystal's impedance is inductive, as shown in Fig. 5.18,
and together with C_2, it provides a 180° phase lag. Thus, the crystal can
provide anything from a 0° to 180° phase lag by just a small increase or
decrease in frequency from series resonance.

In reality, of course, the amplifier provides slightly more than a 180°
phase shift, due to the transistor's internal capacitance and storage time,
and the R_1C_1 integrating network provides something less than a 90°
phase shift. Figure 5.19 shows more practical phase-shift values to be
expected in a Pierce circuit. The crystal typically operates inductively,
about 5–40 ppm above series resonance, because the actual phase lag of
R_1C_1 is significantly less than 90°.

There is a close correlation in the Pierce between the circuit's short-
term frequency stability and the crystal's internal series resistance R_s.
The lower the crystal's resistance at series resonance, the smaller the
frequency shift needed to change the crystal's impedance from capacitive to inductive (or vice versa) and correct any phase errors around the
loop.

It was mentioned earlier that the oscillator's frequency is relatively
insensitive to small changes in resistance and capacitance values. The
reason is that the phase lag of each RC integrating network (R_1C_1 and

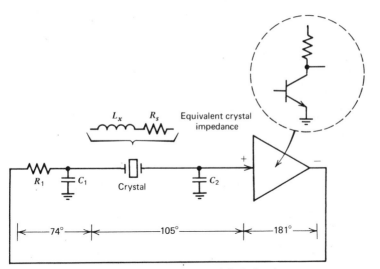

Figure 5.19. Pierce circuit, actual operation (slightly above series resonance).

R_sC_2) is much greater than 45°, and a small change in either the resistance or capacitance of such a network introduces only a very small change in its phase lag. Changes in either R or C will introduce significant gain changes, of course, but only small changes in phase.

To design a Pierce oscillator, the frequency of oscillation and the crystal's internal series resistance R_s must be known. The crystal's internal series resistance need be known only approximately. This can be obtained by referring to Fig. 2.3, which gives the maximum series resistance of crystals at various frequencies. The typical crystal's internal series resistance is about ⅔ of the maximum value given in Fig. 2.3. The time constants of the two RC phase-shifting networks should be made as large as possible. This makes their phase shifts as independent as possible of any changes in resistance or capacitance values. Such networks have large gain losses, which mean that the transistor used for the amplifier should be selected on the basis of having the highest possible gain in order to compensate for these losses.

The highest gain RF transistors have a minimum current gain h_{FE} of 100. This allows a maximum amplifier voltage gain of about 50. To maintain oscillation, we need a net loop gain of 1.5–2, which gives a gain of about 50/1.7 = 30 to cover the losses of the two RC networks. Dividing this gain of 30 equally between them allows each to have a gain loss of about 5.5. This defines the capacitive shunt reactance in each RC network as 1/5.5 or 0.18 its series-resistance value. Thus, the shunt capacitance C_2 on the crystal's output should have a reactance of 0.18 the crystal's series resistance. With the known frequency of oscillation, the actual capacitance value can be calculated.

To minimize loading effects of the crystal's internal series resistance R_s on C_1, the reactance of C_1 should be much lower than the series resistance of the crystal, say $\frac{1}{5}$ of it, which means that C_1 should be approximately equal to C_2. This also means that R_1 should be approximately equal to the crystal's internal series resistance R_s. R_1 frequently turns out to be a little low for the transistor to drive conveniently, so it is often fudged upward a little to a value that the transistor can drive more easily, and the impedance of C_1 is fudged upward along with it to avoid any additional gain loss.

The preceding describes a typical Pierce circuit at middle frequencies. At low frequencies, the amplifier's input stage must be a FET to avoid resistive loading of the crystal's high internal series resistance R_s at low frequencies. And at high frequencies, the amplifier's output stage must be an emitter follower in order to be able to drive the low impedance of the crystal at high frequencies.

For harmonic operation, either of two approaches can be used. With the first approach, a resonant LC tank tuned to the desired harmonic is incorporated somewhere within the amplifier. The second approach uses the circuit shown in Fig. 5.20.

The circuit in Fig. 5.20 is the same as the one in Fig. 5.18 except that an inductor L_1 has been added in parallel with C_1. L_1 is picked to parallel resonate with C_1 at some intermediate frequency (say halfway) between desired harmonic oscillation frequency and the next lower odd harmonic. At the desired harmonic frequency, the impedance of L_1 will then be high enough with respect to the impedance of C_1 so that it can be neglected, and $R_1 C_1$ will act as an integrating network and provide the desired 90° (idealistically speaking) phase lag. Thus, the circuit will os-

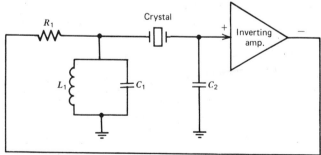

Figure 5.20. Pierce circuit for harmonic operation. $L_1 C_1$ is *not* tuned to the harmonic oscillation frequency.

cillate normally at the desired harmonic. At all lower harmonics, however, the impedance of L_1 will be lower than the impedance of C_1. Then, C_1 will be negligible instead of L_1, and $R_1 L_1$ will act as a differentiating network, providing 90° of phase lead instead of phase lag. The circuit will not oscillate at any of these lower harmonics because the total phase shift around the loop at these lower frequencies is now 180°, which provides negative feedback and stabilizes the circuit instead of making it oscillate.

The shunt inductance scheme in Fig. 5.20 is useful at medium and high frequencies, but it is redundant at VHF. Above 20 MHz, the amplifier has to use a tuned LC tank as a load to get any gain at all, and this same LC tank can be used to select the desired harmonic without adding an extra inductor in front of the crystal.

The Pierce can be made to oscillate exactly at series resonance rather than just slightly above it by using the circuit in Fig. 5.21. The technique is to use three RC lag networks, each providing a 60° phase lag. In each RC lag network, capacitance C is determined by setting its capacitive reactance equal to $0.5R$ in order to give the 60° phase lag required. Nominally, $R_1 = R_2 = R_s$, and $C_1 = C_2 = C_3$. Because of loading effects of each RC network on the preceding one, capacitance values of C_1 and C_3 will have to be shifted a little to provide the 60° phase lag needed in each RC network. The quickest way to do this is by experiment, trimming the values of C_1 and C_3 to get the desired 60° phase lag in each network. A

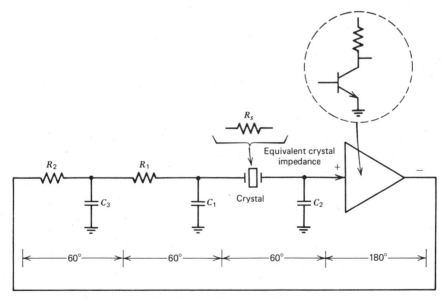

Figure 5.21. Pierce at exact series resonance.

scope is used to measure the actual phase shifts obtained. Capacitance values can also be determined by mathematical circuit analysis.

The Pierce circuit in Fig. 5.21 can be made to oscillate below series resonance as well as exactly at resonance. The only change required is increasing the phase lags of R_2C_3 and R_1C_1 to a little more than 60°.

The circuit in Fig. 5.21 requires less amplifier gain than other Pierce circuits, which is helpful if the amplifier to be used is a little short of gain. Each 60° RC phase-lag network has a gain loss of 0.5X, and an amplifier gain of 16 will provide a net loop gain of two, which is sufficient for proper oscillation.

5.9. PIERCE-IC

This section covers implementing the Pierce oscillator with integrated circuits, but does not discuss how the Pierce circuit works, which is treated in Section 5.8.

The Pierce amplifier can be built using digital logic elements in CMOS, TTL, and ECL. The basic frequency range of each technology applies to crystal oscillators; that is, CMOS for low frequencies, TTL for medium frequencies, and ECL for medium and high frequencies. Two primary considerations in each technology are (1) obtaining the high amplifier gain required by the Pierce circuit and (2) the amount of internal phase shift or time delay in the amplifier (or inverter). Each technology will be discussed in turn.

In CMOS, both the gain and frequency bandwidth of a single inverter stage vary widely from manufacturer to manufacturer. The A series are unusable for oscillator purposes because of their low inverter gains of 1.1–2 and their lack of output drive power. B series inverters have gains of 10–30. The widest bandwidth (i.e., the least delay) CMOS inverter tested was manufactured by Solid State Scientific, followed by National Semiconductor's 74C series.

A single CMOS inverter is frequently used as the amplifier in the Pierce circuit in Fig. 5.22. The gain of a CMOS inverter is too low to use the normal Pierce circuit in Fig. 5.19, so the resistor R_1 is eliminated and replaced with the internal output resistance R_0 of the CMOS inverter, as shown in Fig. 5.22. This reduces gain loss and allows operation with a single CMOS inverter. The inverter's output voltage swings between zero and one are then highly sloped, and amplitude is sometimes below normal. A second CMOS inverter is added as an external isolation amplifier in order to square up the output signal and ensure getting a full rail-to-rail voltage swing.

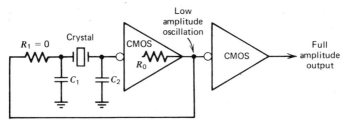

Figure 5.22.   Pierce in CMOS. R_1 is replaced by the inverter's output resistance R_0.

Using the CMOS inverter's output resistance to replace R_1 in Fig. 5.19 has the disadvantage that the crystal is driven at a much higher voltage level than it would be in a normal Pierce circuit. At frequencies above 2 MHz, the crystal's power dissipation should be checked to make sure it is within the maximum dissipation limit.

In TTL, only a voltage comparator IC can be used to make a Pierce oscillator. Ordinary TTL inverters have gains of only 3–9X, which is not enough to make a Pierce out of a single inverter. Cascading three inverters in series to increase gain will not work either, because very bad parasitic oscillations occur during the switching interval when a TTL inverter's output voltage moves less than a full voltage swing. TTL line receivers will not work because their gain of about 15X is too low. In order to make a TTL oscillator using something other than a voltage comparator IC, it is necessary to use the series-resonant two-inverter-type circuit, which is described in Section 5.7.

In ECL, a single line receiver does not have enough gain to make a Pierce oscillator. But three 10114 line receivers can be cascaded in series to get enough gain. A single 10114 receiver has a gain of 3–6X. The 10116 and 10216 are apparently constructed differently than the 10114, since the units tested showed wider gain variations than the 10114 and exhibited relatively large gain differences between a receiver's two outputs (normal and inverted).

Although a relatively high gain may be desirable in an IC for oscillator circuitry, it should be said that a high gain per stage is undesirable in digital circuitry, which is what many of these ICs are designed for. High gain increases the tendency for spurious oscillations (caused by stray feedback) during the digital switching interval. A low stage gain of 1.5–3X is sufficient in a digital IC, since the primary purpose of gain in a digital IC is to prevent a low amplitude signal from propagating throughout the system.

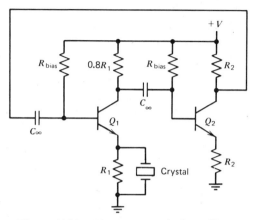

Figure 5.23.   Emitter coupled oscillator.

5.10.   EMITTER COUPLED

The emitter coupled oscillator is a series-resonant circuit, and a basic schematic is shown in Fig. 5.23. The oscillator has a positive feedback amplifier with a loop gain of slightly less than one without the crystal, so that the circuit will not oscillate by itself. Loop gain is controlled by the ratio of the collector to emitter resistances in each transistor stage. In the second stage, it is convenient to make emitter and collector resistances (R_2 and R_2) equal to each other, giving a stage gain of 1X. The second stage inverts the signal and provides positive feedback.

In the first stage, the collector resistor $0.8R_1$ is made a little smaller than the emitter resistor R_1 in order to give an overall loop gain of 0.8X. The value of the emitter resistor R_1 is set equal to about twice the crystal's internal series resistance R_s. When the crystal is tied in parallel with R_1, the effective resistance of the emitter resistor is reduced at series resonance, since the crystal's internal resistance R_s is in parallel with R_1. This raises both stage gain and overall loop gain to about 2X, and the circuit oscillates at the crystal's series-resonant frequency.

An advantage of this circuit is that the crystal sees a very low resistance load. This low resistance load consists mostly of the emitter's input resistance, which is much lower than R_1. A disadvantage is that circuit waveforms vary with the circuit's stray capacitance, because loop gain is almost high enough to oscillate at any frequency.

5.11.   MODIFIED MEACHAM

The Meacham [5, 17] is a resistance-bridge circuit, as shown in Fig. 5.24. The crystal is located in one arm of the bridge. A tungsten lamp, located

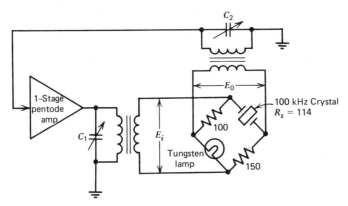

Figure 5.24. Meacham resistance bridge.

in another arm of the bridge, is used as a variable resistance-amplitude control. There is no voltage out of the bridge at exact bridge balance, so it operates slightly off-balance—just enough to get a loop gain of exactly 1X around the amplifier circuit. The tungsten lamp's resistance increases with the applied voltage, and its variable resistance automatically controls loop gain at exactly 1X. This provides a constant sine wave excitation voltage to the crystal. The amplifier has a large voltage gain E_i/E_0 of 422X.

Clapp's version [18] of the Meacham is shown in Fig. 5.25. The advantage of Clapp's arrangement is the elimination of transformers by using a split-load phase inverter to drive the bridge. Vacuum tube V_2 in Fig. 5.25 has equal cathode and plate voltages of opposite phase for

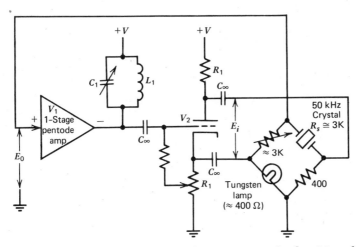

Figure 5.25. Clapp's version of the Meacham resistance bridge. Note that it has no transformers.

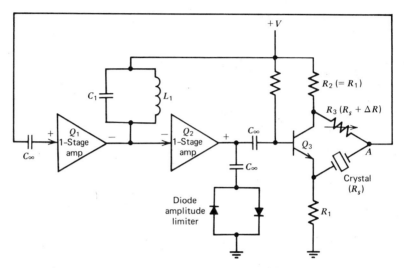

Figure 5.26. Modified Meacham half-bridge.

driving the bridge. Clapp's amplifier also has a large voltage gain E_i/E_0 of about 300X. Both of these circuits use a single stage of amplification, a pentode vacuum tube.

If something other than a tungsten filament is used for amplitude control, the Meacham can be simplified further into the half-bridge arrangement shown in Fig. 5.26, which uses a diode clamp for amplitude control. A thermistor (which has a negative temperature coefficient of resistance) can also be used for amplitude control by putting it in the half-bridge in place of R_3. Oscillation amplitude must be at least four times greater if a thermistor is used rather than a diode clamp, since the thermistor requires a minimum of 4–6 Vp-p to properly activate its negative resistance characteristic. Greater oscillation amplitude increases power dissipation in the crystal, which is undesirable.

The advantage of the Meacham is its extremely good short-term frequency stability. This can be seen by looking at Fig. 5.26 and treating the output of the half-bridge at point A as a summing point for two input signals. At series resonance, the amplitude of the positive signal from the emitter of Q_3 is limited at A by the crystal's internal series resistance R_s. At the same time, the amplitude of the negative signal from the collector of Q_3 is limited at point A by R_3, which if set equal to R_s, will cancel out the positive resistive signal from the emitter. What is happening is that the crystal's internal series resistance (but not its internal inductance or capacitance) is being canceled out by the reverse-phase signal through R_3. The crystal's in-circuit Q increases, and its effective internal resistance decreases. In theory, with exact cancellation of the crystal's internal resistance by R_3, the crystal's Q would approach infinity. In practice, this cannot happen, since R_3 must be slightly larger than R_s to get some signal gain (greater than zero) through the bridge. With high amplifier gain, less gain is required through the bridge to maintain oscillation, and R_3 can cancel out a larger percentage of the crystal's internal resistance. Thus, there is a strong advantage in using the highest possible amplifier gain, since that will give the highest possible cancellation of the crystal's resistance and the highest in-circuit Q.

The disadvantage of the Meacham is that it has a strong tendency to oscillate parasitically at high frequencies. It is very difficult to design a stable Meacham circuit. The cause of this can be seen in the bridge's gain versus frequency transfer function, as shown in Fig. 5.27. Figure 5.27 shows that the gain at the crystal's resonant frequency is much less than 1X and 1X at all other frequencies. To oscillate, the circuit has to have enough amplifier gain to bring the low bridge gain at resonance up to a net loop gain of at least 1 or 2X, which means that the gain at all other frequencies is undesirably much higher than this. To prevent parasitic oscillation, this high loop gain at frequencies away from resonance must be reduced to less than 1X while introducing less than 180° additional phase shift. To do this involves consideration of Bode's stability criteria for feedback-type amplifiers, which is too broad a subject to cover here.

Figure 5.24 shows that Meacham used two resonant LC tank circuits to roll off loop gain at frequencies away from resonance. Figure 5.25 shows that Clapp, with a lower loop gain, used only one resonant LC tank circuit to reduce the gain at frequencies away from resonance. The

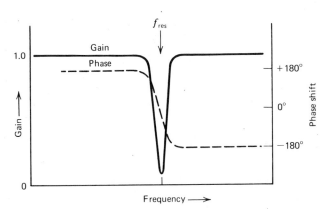

Figure 5.27.   Resistance bridge gain and phase versus frequency for the normal operating condition $R_3 > R_s$.

modified Meacham half-bridge circuit in Fig. 5.26 uses one resonant LC tank to roll off loop gain at frequencies away from resonance.

The modified Meacham half-bridge circuit has two additional characteristics of interest. The first is that the sequence of placing the resonant LC tank before the diode amplitude clamp in Fig. 5.26 is significant, since this provides a square wave drive to the crystal. Reversing the sequence will provide a sine wave drive to the crystal. The second characteristic of interest is that the two output signals from the split-load phase inverter Q_3 in Fig. 5.26 do not have to be of equal amplitude. Necessary bridge balance is maintained by adjusting the ratio of R_3 to the crystal's internal series resistance R_s in proportion to the amplitude ratio of Q_3's emitter and collector signals.

It turns out to be very helpful to reduce the collector's output signal from Q_3 in Fig. 5.26 by a factor of two or more with respect to that from Q_3's emitter. This is done by reducing the value of R_2 to one-half (or one-fourth or one-eighth) of R_1. Doing this has three advantages. First, R_3 is reduced proportionately with R_2 to maintain bridge balance. This lowers the crystal's load resistance, which consists mostly of R_3, and improves short-term frequency stability. Second, all frequencies away from resonance pass through R_3 and the collector of Q_3 rather than through the crystal. Reducing R_2 with respect to R_1 reduces loop gain at all frequencies away from resonance without affecting loop gain at resonance. This helps the high-frequency parasitic oscillation problem considerably. And third, R_1 feeds back to the base of Q_3 a larger percentage of the collector's output voltage, which broadens the bandwidth of the inverter stage Q_3 and reduces the collector's phase-shift error at high frequencies. This helps the high-frequency parasitic oscillation problem.

5.12. SPECIAL OSCILLATOR ICs

There is an assortment of special ICs available that are specifically designed to be used as crystal oscillators. Most of them try to cover a wide frequency range of 10 to 1 or so with a fixed circuit, which is very difficult to do. The crystal's load resistance usually matches the crystal at the low end of the IC's frequency range, but it is frequently too large at the high-frequency end. Special ICs use all of the IC technologies: CMOS, TTL, ECL, and LINEAR. Two of them incorporate an AGC (automatic gain control) circuit to keep oscillation amplitude low and minimize frequency drift due to crystal heating. This is a nice touch when implemented properly. Three of the special ICs use the common base cir-

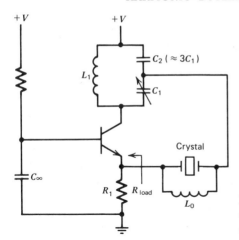

Figure 5.28. Butler common base, capacitive tap. L_0 is not needed below about 70 MHz.

cuit, and one uses the series-resonant circuit; another uses the Pierce and the other, the emitter coupled circuit.

5.13. HARMONIC–BUTLER COMMON BASE

The Butler common base circuit is a VHF harmonic oscillator, operating at or near series resonance; a basic schematic is shown in Fig. 5.28. The circuit is used at frequencies between 20–200 MHz. It uses a common base amplifier, which is an inherently stable design at high frequencies. The collector load is an LC tank, detuned a significant amount off resonance at the desired harmonic. Starting at 50–100 MHz, the impedance of the crystal's shunt terminal capacitance C_0 (about 5 pF) starts approaching the size of the crystal's internal series resistance R_s and provides an alternative path around the crystal, thereby shorting it out. So above about 70 MHz, an inductor L_0 is tied across the crystal to resonate with the crystal's terminal capacitance C_0 and tune it out of the circuit.

The load resistance seen by the crystal in Fig. 5.28 is the parallel sum of the emitter resistor R_1 and the emitter's input resistance. The gain of the transistor is the ratio of the LC tank circuit's impedance divided by the resistance of the emitter resistor R_1. Practical LC tank circuit impedances are relatively low at VHF, so it is necessary to keep R_1 small to get enough gain for oscillation. The internal series resistance R_s of crystals at 20–200 MHz is 20–200 Ω, respectively. A good load resistance for a crystal is about 25–50% of its internal series resistance or 5–50 Ω. The emitter's input resistance is lower than R_1 and is set to the desired crystal load value by adjusting the emitter current. With a load resistance of

$0.33R_s$, this gives $(1 + 0.33)/0.33$ or a 4 to 1 gain loss by the voltage-divider action of the load resistance with the crystal's internal series resistance R_s. The source impedance driving the crystal is mostly capacitive and is one to two times the impedance of C_2, depending on the value of C_1.

The source impedance at the collector is much too high to drive the low impedance of a typical VHF crystal. So, figuratively speaking, the crystal is tapped down on the LC tank circuit to (1) reduce the source impedance seen by the crystal and (2) reduce the crystal drive level and keep the crystal within its power dissipation limit. Experimentally, tapping the crystal across about ¼ of the tank circuit seems to be about optimum from the practical standpoint of maximum energy transfer and minimum gain loss; that is, in Fig. 5.28, let $C_2 = 3C_1$. If tapped down much further, total gain loss around the circuit gets too high, and it will no longer oscillate.

Tapping down the crystal on the collector's LC tank drastically changes the operation of the LC tank. The source impedance driving the crystal drops down from 1000 Ω to 5–15 Ω, a much lower value than would be expected. Although it gets the point across, the idea of tapping down on the LC tank is too simplistic to describe what really happens when the crystal is tied to an intermediate point part way across the LC tank. What really happens is as follows. Let us rearrange Fig. 5.28 as shown in Fig. 5.29. Referring to Fig. 5.29, the crystal's internal series resistance R_s is approximately equal to the impedance of C_2, so that C_2 is partially shorted out from the LC tank. As a result, C_2 has very little effect on the resonant frequency of the LC tank over a very wide range of capacitance values. The effective LC tank circuit becomes L_1C_1, which the crystal sees as a (near) series-resonant circuit of low impedance. At

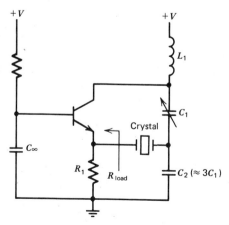

Figure 5.29. Common base circuit in Fig. 5.28 rearranged. L_0 has been left out for clarity.

the same time, the transistor's collector sees the L_1C_1 tank as a (near) parallel-resonant circuit of high impedance. Since the crystal wants to see a low source impedance and the collector wants to see a high load impedance, both like what they see, and the circuit ends up with a good impedance transformation ratio that depends on the Q of the L_1C_1 tank. This explanation of circuit operation has been verified both experimentally and analytically. Tuning the tank circuit depends almost entirely on L_1 and C_1 and is essentially independent of C_2.

Does it make any difference if the crystal is tapped down on the inductor in the LC tank instead of on the capacitor? Yes, it does. Figure 5.30 shows an inductively tapped circuit. Tapping down on the inductor gives a phase lag to the amplifier circuit, while tapping down on the capacitor gives a phase lead. In both cases, there is a phase lag from the emitter to the collector, caused by operating the LC tank off resonance. The phase lead of a capacitor tap subtracts from the emitter-to-collector phase lag and allows the crystal to oscillate either at or above series resonance. The phase lag of an inductive tap just adds to the emitter-to-collector phase lag and forces the crystal to oscillate below series resonance, where it can provide a phase lead to compensate the two other phase lags in the circuit to zero. The end result is that a capacitive tap allows crystal operation above, at, or slightly below series resonance, while the inductive tap allows crystal operation only below series resonance. These phase-lead and phase-lag effects are analyzed and discussed in detail in Sections 7.6 and 7.7.

Tapping into the capacitive side of the LC tank introduces a lot of parasitic oscillations into the circuit. These parasitic oscillations are the biggest drawback to the capacitive tap version of the circuit. Most, but

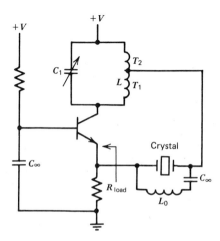

Figure 5.30. Butler common base, inductive tap. L_0 is not needed below about 70 MHz. T_2 is normally $\frac{1}{5}$ to $\frac{1}{6}$ of the total coil turns.

not all, of these parasitic oscillations can be suppressed by resistive loading of the LC tank and careful attention to circuit layout. In contrast, the inductive tap gives clean circuit operation without any parasitics and seems to give equal frequency stability, but its oscillation frequency is about 4 ppm lower.

Another difficulty with Butler's common base circuit is that it will only oscillate over a relatively narrow range of collector current. If the current is too small, the circuit will not oscillate because loop gain is too low. And if the current is too large, two undesirable things happen. First, the collector's LC tank gets shunted with a low resistance from the large collector current, which cuts the gain. And secondly, the emitter's input resistance, which makes up most of the crystal's load resistance and is an inverse function of the emitter current, becomes much smaller. This also cuts circuit gain, so much so that the circuit will not oscillate.

A third difficulty is that it is hard to get the crystal drive voltage down low enough to keep it from overdriving the emitter into cutoff and to keep crystal dissipation within its limit. Figure 2.5 shows that the maximum drive voltage for many crystals between 20–100 MHz at series resonance is 0.2 Vrms or 0.6 Vp-p. We can tap down the crystal further on the LC tank in Figs. 5.28 or 5.29, but this reduces loop gain, which is already on the low side, and the circuit may quit oscillating. One solution is to shunt the inductor in the LC tank with two parallel diodes of reversed polarity, as shown in Fig. 10.17. This limits oscillation amplitude without cutting loop gain. Another solution is to reduce the power supply voltage from 5 to 2 or 3 V.

For the Butler common base circuit to oscillate, experimental data indicate that the impedance of the inductor L_1 in the LC tank in Fig. 5.28 should be a certain fixed value (within a factor of 2 or so) regardless of the frequency. This means that the inductive value of L_1 should vary inversely with frequency. Table 5.2 lists some usable inductance values for L_1 at several frequencies from 20 to 100 MHz. The inductance to be used at intermediate frequencies can be interpolated from values given

TABLE 5.2
Some Usable Inductance Values for the L_1C_1 Tank
in the Butler Circuit in Fig. 5.28

Oscillation Frequency (MHz)	Usable Range of Inductance for L_1
20	0.47–2.4 μH
50	0.22–1.0 μH
100	0.10–0.47 μH

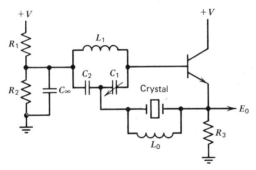

Figure 5.31. Butler emitter follower, capacitive tap. L_0 is not needed at frequencies below about 70 MHz.

in Table 5.2. The circuit seems to work better if the lower inductance value at each frequency is used.

5.14. HARMONIC–BUTLER EMITTER FOLLOWER

The Butler emitter follower is a VHF harmonic oscillator, operating at or near series resonance; a basic schematic is shown in Fig. 5.31. The circuit is useful mostly at frequencies between 20 and 200 MHz. The amplifier has a gain of one; the oscillator's loop gain is provided by L_1 and C_1 operating near series resonance. Tapping the crystal into the capacitive side of the LC tank gives a phase lead, and the crystal then oscillates either at or slightly above series resonance. Starting at 50–100 MHz, the impedance of the crystal's terminal capacitance C_0 (about 5 pF) approaches the crystal's series resistance R_s and provides an alternative path around the crystal, tending to short it out. So above about 70 MHz, an inductor L_0 is tied across the crystal to parallel resonate with the crystal's terminal capacitance C_0 and tune it out of the circuit.

Although Butler's emitter follower circuit is not so well-known as his common base circuit, his emitter follower circuit offers many practical advantages over the common base arrangement. Tapping down the crystal on the LC tank increases the oscillator's loop gain instead of decreasing it, as in the common base circuit. The amplifier's gain of one gives a stable gain configuration that is independent of bias variations and always works with any transistor. The emitter follower circuit can be operated at frequencies down to 1 kHz, whereas the lowest frequency of the common base circuit is limited to about 8 or 10 MHz by the effect of the emitter's low load resistance on the crystal (high gain loss).

The built-in feedback of an emitter follower circuit gives a very wide amplifier bandwidth, allowing the circuit to operate at higher frequencies than what the common base circuit will provide. There are no parasitic oscillation effects because of the amplifier's low gain of one and its built-in feedback stabilization. Compared to the common base amplifier, the undesirable oscillation damping provided by DC current flow through the inductor is reduced by the transistor's current gain h_{fe} of 20–100. And while loop gain drops slightly with a heavy emitter current, the emitter follower is not limited to a narrow operating current range, as is the common base circuit. At any given frequency, a wider range of inductance values can be used with the emitter follower circuit than with the common base arrangement.

A practical Butler emitter follower is shown in Fig. 5.32. It operates as follows: L_1C_1 form a resonant circuit operating near (but not at) series resonance, providing a low input impedance to the crystal and a high output impedance to the transistor base. All of the oscillator's loop gain comes from L_1 and C_1 operating near series resonance. The value of C_2 has almost no effect on the resonant tuning of the LC tank circuit, which seems to be due to the shunting effect of the crystal's low impedance on C_2.

From the emitter's viewpoint in Fig. 5.32, C_2 is effectively in series with the crystal, which raises the oscillation frequency slightly above series resonance. It is desirable to make C_2 large in order to give it a low impedance, which moves the oscillation frequency down closer to series resonance. There is an optimum value for C_2: If C_2 is too large, it short circuits the amplifier gain loop and cuts the gain. If C_2 is too

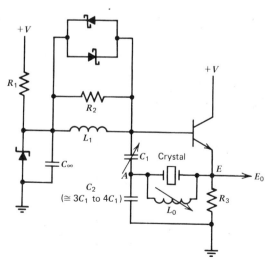

Figure 5.32.   Practical Butler emitter follower circuit.

small, it starts reacting with the inductive input impedance of L_1C_1, raising the crystal's load impedance to an undesirably high value. The optimum impedance of C_2 is about 0.5–1 times the crystal's series resistance R_s.

R_2 gives the emitter follower a low output resistance for driving the crystal load. The two Schottky diodes across L_1 limit oscillation amplitude to (1) keep the crystal's power dissipation within its rating and (2) keep the transistor conducting over the complete oscillation waveform and maintain a low emitter drive resistance for the crystal over a complete cycle. The crystal's load capacitor C_2 is tied to the grounded end of the emitter resistor R_3 rather than to the Zener bias supply, as was shown in Fig. 5.31. Tying C_2 to the grounded end of R_3 gives a shorter crystal drive loop from the emitter, and the circuit performs better. The base bias voltage is stabilized with a Zener diode to reduce frequency shift when the power supply voltage changes. This bias stabilization reduces frequency sensitivity to power supply changes by an order of magnitude.

Selection of L and C values is as follows: C_2 is selected so that its reactance is equal to about 0.5 to 1 times the crystal's series resistance. C_1 should be ⅓ to ¼ of C_2. If C_1 is one-half of C_2, the crystal's load impedance is undesirably high; if C_1 is one-eighth of C_2, loop gain is too low. L_1 is selected for approximate series resonance with C_1. There is an experimental cross-check on the correct values of C_1 and C_2. In Fig. 5.32, C_1 and C_2 are in the right range when voltage at point A is 30–70% of the voltage at point E, indicating that the crystal's load impedance is approximately equal to the crystal's internal impedance.

Figure 5.33 shows an alternative emitter follower circuit with the

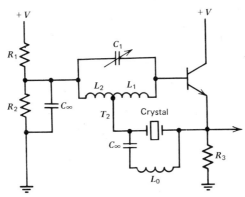

Figure 5.33. Butler emitter follower, inductive tap. T_2 is normally ⅕ to ⅙ of the total coil turns.

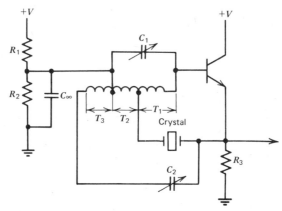

Figure 5.34. Alternative compensation scheme for crystal's shunt terminal capacitance C_0.

crystal tapped into the inductive side of the LC tank circuit rather than into the capacitive side. T_2 is set at about $1/5$ to $1/6$ of the total turns on the inductor. This provides a phase lag in the amplifier circuit loop, and the crystal then oscillates either at or slightly below series resonance. The L and C circuit values are selected on a basis similar to that used for the capacitive tap circuit.

Figure 5.34 shows an alternative scheme proposed by Butler [6] to compensate for the crystal's terminal capacitance C_0. Above 50–100 MHz, the crystal's shunt terminal capacitance C_0 provides an undesirable shunt path around the crystal's internal frequency-controlling elements. Rather than resonating an inductance L_0 in parallel with C_0, the idea here is to cancel the effects of C_0 by adding an equal voltage of opposite phase through an equivalent capacitance C_2 to the LC tank. The reversed phase is obtained by extending the inductance winding in the LC tank below AC ground. The emitter signal is then fed to this reversed polarity terminal through a capacitance C_2. If $T_2 = T_3$ and $C_2 = C_0$ (the crystal's shunt capacitance), then the shunt signal through the crystal's capacitance is canceled out. One drawback to this arangement is the increased capacitive loading on the emitter, which is already heavily loaded by the crystal impedance. As will be shown in Section 10.24, this compensation scheme does not work out very well in practice.

CHAPTER SIX

SHORT-TERM FREQUENCY STABILITY

This chapter shows the relationship between short-term frequency stability and in-circuit Q. Section 6.1 describes the effect of the crystal's external load resistance on in-circuit Q and useful differences between series and parallel equivalents of a combined resistive-capacitive load on a crystal. Section 6.2 presents experimental data showing that the equivalent series resistance of the crystal load is the component to be minimized for maximum short-term frequency stability and shows what values of parallel-load resistance will give good in-circuit Q.

6.1.   IN-CIRCUIT Q

Crystal Q is important because it controls the short-term frequency stability of the oscillator; the basic mechanism of how it does this is as follows. A small amount of energy is dumped into the crystal on every cycle. This energy in the crystal oscillates back and forth thousands of times before gradually dying out, so that the actual voltage or current out of the crystal at any given instant is the average of energy or frequency dumped into the crystal over thousands of cycles. The more cycles that the readout voltage or current is averaged over, the more constant the readout frequency. Q is a measure of how long energy in the crystal oscillates back and forth before dying out. Thus, the higher the Q, the better the short-term frequency stability of the crystal.

The Q of a crystal in a circuit is usually less than the Q of the crystal alone, since the circuit introduces resistive losses into the crystal's oscillation loop. To minimize Q losses, we can keep the crystal's external load resistance relatively low; that is, equal to or less than the crystal's internal series resistance R_s, so that the in-circuit Q is not degraded by more than a factor of two from the crystal's internal Q. Another approach is to use a reactive load (which is lossless) rather than a resistive one. An example of this is the Pierce circuit, where the external load on the crystal is primarily capacitive rather than resistive. A third approach, which is not widely known, is to use a load resistance that is very large with respect to the reactance of the crystal's terminal shunt capacitance C_0, so that the external crystal load is effectively capacitive (and low loss) rather than resistive. In general, the technique of using a reactive load on the crystal instead of a resistive one is very effective in obtaining a high in-circuit Q and improves short-term frequency stability.

In describing the load on a crystal, it is important to distinguish between two equivalent representations, that is, as a parallel load with resistance and capacitance in parallel with each other or as an equivalent series load with resistance and capacitance in series with each other. For maximizing in-circuit Q, it turns out that we want to minimize the equivalent *series* load resistance, as is shown in the next section.

Figure 6.1*a* shows a commonly used crystal circuit, with source and load resistances, load capacitance, and the crystal's shunt terminal capacitance C_0 indicated. From the crystal's point of view, the load impedance across the crystal's terminals is in series with its internal L_x and C_x components, as shown in Fig. 6.1*b*. Hence, a reactive load impedance on the crystal will change the resonant frequency by changing the net total series inductance and/or capacitance in the crystal's oscillation loop. It is also apparent from Fig. 6.1*b* that from the viewpoint of the crystal's internal frequency controlling elements L_x and C_x, the crystal's shunt terminal capacitance C_0 should be considered as part of the load on the crystal, and not as part of its internal frequency-controlling elements.

From the crystal's viewpoint, it is easier to use the equivalent series $R_s C_s$ load network for determining in-circuit Q, as shown in the right-half of Fig. 6.1*c*. But from a circuit-design viewpoint, it is easier to use the parallel $R_p C_p$ load network, as shown in the left-half of Fig. 6.1*c*. To tie the two viewpoints together, we need to do some parallel to series (and vice versa) conversions of the crystal's load impedance.

The minimum value of C_p is the crystal's shunt terminal capacitance C_0, about 5 pF. Using a fixed value of 5 pF for C_p and a 1-MHz oscillation frequency, Fig. 6.2 shows equivalent series values of $(R_s)_{\text{load}}$ and C_s for various values of parallel load resistance R_p. To maximize the crystal's in-circuit Q, we should minimize $(R_s)_{\text{load}}$ in the right-half of Fig. 6.1*c*. Figure 6.2 shows that either low or high values of R_p will give acceptably

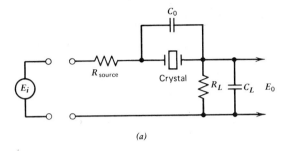

(a)

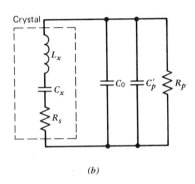

(b)

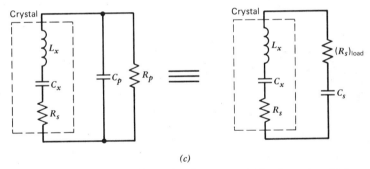

(c)

Figure 6.1. Equivalent crystal RC load circuits in both series $(R_s)_{\text{load}}$ C_s and parallel $R_p C_p$ load forms: (a) typical crystal load circuit, (b) intermediate load circuit, and (c) equivalent load circuits.

low values of $(R_s)_{\text{load}}$ but that intermediate values of R_p near 32K Ω will give unacceptably high values of $(R_s)_{\text{load}}$, with a resulting very low in-circuit Q.

By converting equivalent values of $(R_s)_{\text{load}}$ into circuit Q, where

$$Q = \frac{2\pi(\text{frequency})\, L_x}{(R_s)_{\text{crystal}} + (R_s)_{\text{load}}},$$

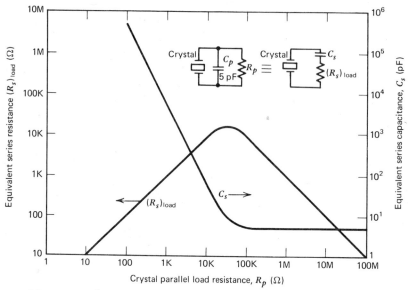

Figure 6.2. Equivalent series $(R_s)_{\text{load}}$ and C_s values for a parallel $R_p C_p$ network at 1 MHz. C_p is fixed at 5 pF, R_p is varied from 10 Ω to 100 MΩ.

Fig. 6.3 shows the variation of circuit Q with parallel load resistance R_p. Figure 6.3 shows that circuit Q is high for both low and high values of R_p but very low for R_p values anywhere near 32K Ω. In fact, for circuit Q to be half or more of its maximum value, R_p has to be more than two orders of magnitude higher or lower than 32K Ω. What is happening at 32K Ω? At 32K Ω, parallel resistance R_p is equal to the 32K reactive impedance of parallel capacitance C_p. And when that occurs, the transformation of R_p into its equivalent series value $(R_s)_{\text{load}}$ gives a peak in the series-resistance value $(R_s)_{\text{load}}$, as shown in Fig. 6.2.

Since all quartz crystals have a shunt terminal capacitance C_0 of about 5 pF, we can generalize this parallel-to-series peaking effect to any frequency by saying that for good in-circuit Q the parallel load resistance R_p should be greater or less than the reactance of the crystal's terminal capacitance C_0 by two orders of magnitude. Figure 6.4 is a graph of this relationship, showing good and bad values of parallel resistance R_p for both low and high values of circuit Q. The average value for the crystal's terminal capacitance C_0 was 5 pF, which, with assumed zero load capacitance C_L, is equal to parallel load capacitance C_p. This calculated relationship between parallel load resistance R_p and in-circuit Q is verified by experimental data in the next section.

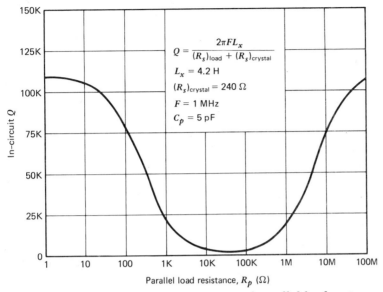

Figure 6.3.   Calculated in-circuit Q versus crystal parallel load resistance R_p.

6.2. MEASUREMENT OF IN-CIRCUIT Q

There are many ways to measure in-circuit Q. The method used here is to suddenly disconnect the crystal from the oscillator circuit and measure the decay of the voltage across the crystal (or the current through it) as a function of time. The measurement of Q is taken as the time required for the voltage across the crystal (or the current through it) to decay to $1/e$ of its initial value. The longer the decay time, the higher the Q.

Figures 6.5 and 6.6 show the envelope of voltage decay across a 1-MHz crystal for various resistive and capacitive loads across the crystal terminals. Loads range from a near open circuit to a short circuit. All waveforms shown are voltage measurements across the crystal except for the short-circuit measurement, which is a current measurement using a Tektronix current probe. The impedance of the current probe is about 0.1 Ω. A mechanical toggle switch was used for switching the crystal out of the circuit, and the bounce of the switch contacts can be seen at the left edge in some of the photographs. Note, in particular, in Fig. 6.5 the very fast decay with a 10K Ω resistive load on the 1-MHz crystal.

If we measure the crystal's relative Q, as indicated by decay rates in the photographs in Figs. 6.5 and 6.6 and plot it as a function of load resistance and capacitance, we obtain the curves shown in Figs. 6.7 and

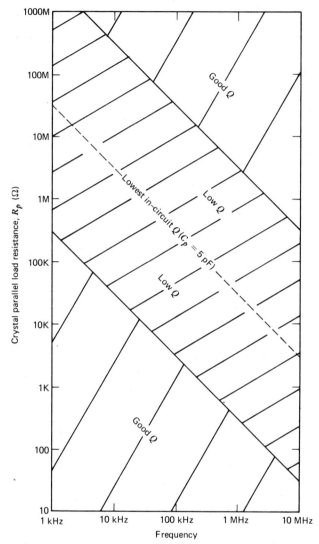

Figure 6.4. Calculated in-circuit Q versus crystal parallel load resistance R_p as a function of frequency.

6.8. Figures 6.7 and 6.8 also show curves of relative crystal Q at four other frequencies: 4, 50, and 100 kHz, and 10 MHz. In order to show all five frequencies, the ordinates in Figs. 6.7 and 6.8 are not plotted in terms of decay time to $1/e$ their initial value but in terms of the total number of oscillation cycles that occur during the $1/e$ decay time. It is probably more relevant to plot the curves this way as well as more convenient.

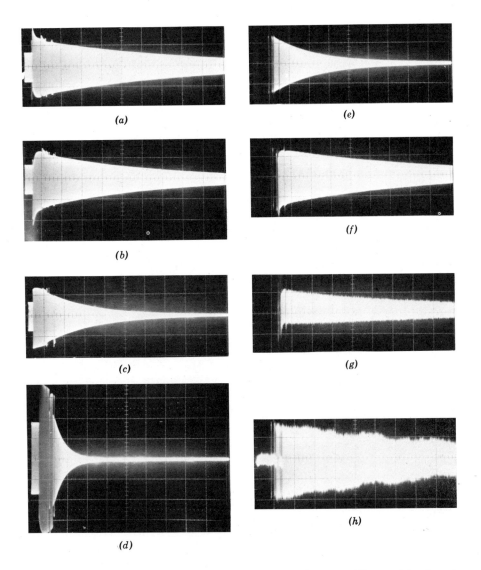

Figure 6.5. Crystal voltage (current) decay as a function of crystal load resistance. All waveforms with same time base of 2 msec/div and crystal disconnected from oscillator circuit. Vertical voltage scales vary. See Fig. 6.11a for test circuit used to obtain these waveforms. (a) 10 MΩ, (b) 1 MΩ, (c) 100K Ω, (d) 10K Ω, (e) 1K Ω, (f) 100 Ω, (g) 10 Ω, and (h) 0 Ω (short circuit).

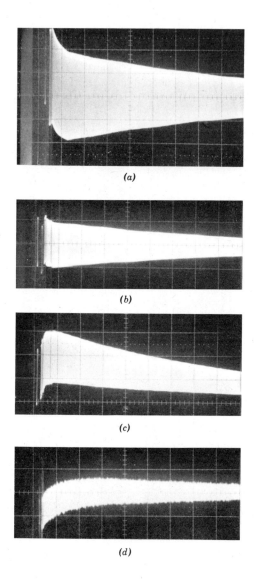

Figure 6.6. Crystal voltage decay as a function of crystal load capacitance. All waveforms with same time base of 2 msec/div and crystal disconnected from oscillator circuit. Vertical voltage scales vary. See Fig. 6.11a for test circuit used to obtain these waveforms. (a) 40 pF, (b) 200 pF, (c) 2000 pF, and (d) 20,000 pF.

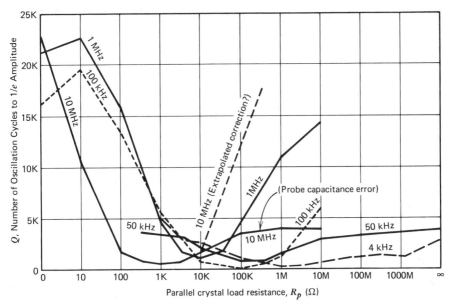

Figure 6.7. Measured crystal Q versus parallel load resistance R_p across the crystal terminals. $C_p = 10$–20 pF.

The Q curve at 10 MHz in Fig. 6.7 contains a measurement error at the high load resistance values, due to the 7 pF of shunt capacitance in the scope probe used. The shunt impedance of the 7 pF of probe capacitance is 3000 Ω at 10 MHz, which completely swamps out the effect of any high resistance values in parallel with it across the crystal. Without the loading of the probe's shunt capacitance, the Q curve of the 10-MHz crystal would probably look more like the dotted line shown in Fig. 6.7.

These experimental curves of crystal Q versus loading in Figs. 6.7 and 6.8 provide considerable information. First, capacitive loading in general gives a higher Q than resistive loading. Second, the best Q is obtained with the crystal short circuited. Third, each of the resistive loading curves in Fig. 6.7 shows a minimum Q at the middle values of resistive loading, and, in each case, parallel resistive loading R_p on the crystal must be increased or decreased by about two orders of magnitude away from the resistance value at minimum Q to get good circuit Q. Figure 6.9 shows these minimum Q resistance values plotted as a function of frequency. Two additional lines have been drawn in Fig. 6.9, which are parallel to the minimum Q line but displaced from it by two orders of magnitude in the parallel load-resistance value. Figure 6.9 shows graphically what resistance-loading values on the crystal will give both good and poor in-circuit Q at any frequency.

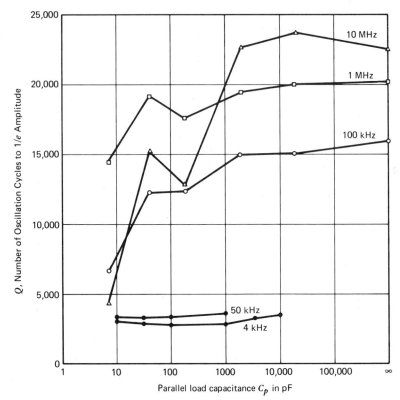

Figure 6.8.   Measured crystal Q versus parallel load capacitance C_p across the crystal terminals. $R_p = 10$–1000 MΩ.

Comparing experimental data in Figs. 6.7 and 6.9 with the calculated data in Figs. 6.3 and 6.4, we see that they are the same except that the experimental values of parallel load resistance are lower than the calculated values by a factor of three at all frequencies. One difference between calculated and measured data is that the calculated value of parallel capacitance C_p is 5 pF while the experimental value is 15 pF, as defined by the impedance of the line of lowest Q in Fig. 6.9. The 15 pF consists of 5 pF of crystal terminal capacitance C_0 plus 7 pF of scope probe capacitance plus 3 pF of stray capacitance. This 3 to 1 difference between the calculated and experimental values for the parallel load capacitance C_p would shift the experimental values of parallel load resistance downward by a factor of three, and this is exactly what a comparison of Fig. 6.9 with Fig. 6.4 shows. The experimental data thus confirms that the low Q at medium resistance values is due to converting

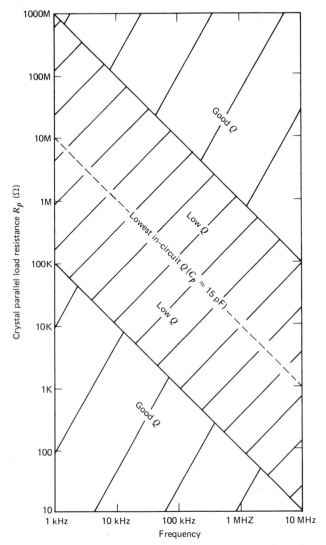

Figure 6.9. Measured effect of a parallel resistive crystal load R_p on Q as a function of frequency.

the parallel RC load values to their equivalent series values. R_p, $(R_s)_{load}$, C_p, and C_s are defined in Fig. 6.1c.

The calculation and measurement of the effects of various loads on crystal operation show the following:

1.   The load tied across the crystal's terminals has a strong effect on the crystal's in-circuit Q.

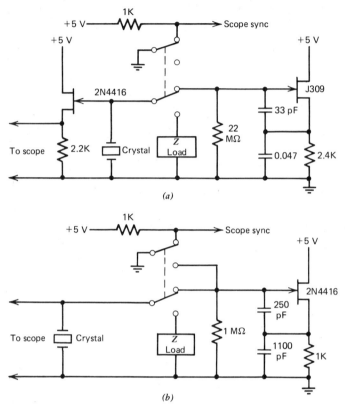

Figure 6.10. Test circuits for measuring crystal loading effects on in-circuit Q: (a) at 4 kHz and 50 kHz and (b) at 100 kHz.

2. The equivalent *series* load resistance $(R_s)_{\text{load}}$, and not the parallel load resistance R_p, is the correct measure of resistive loading effects on the crystal's in-circuit Q.

3. Because a crystal always has a fixed shunt capacitance C_p of 5–15 pF across its terminals, Fig. 6.9 (or Fig. 6.4) is a valid graph of what values of parallel load resistance R_p across the crystal terminals will give a good or poor in-circuit Q.

4. High in-circuit Q can be obtained with either a high or low value of parallel load resistance R_p across the crystal terminals.

5. The worst value of parallel load resistance R_p for any given value of parallel capacitance C_p, that is, the resistance value that will give the lowest possible in-circuit Q, is equal to the reactive impedance of C_p.

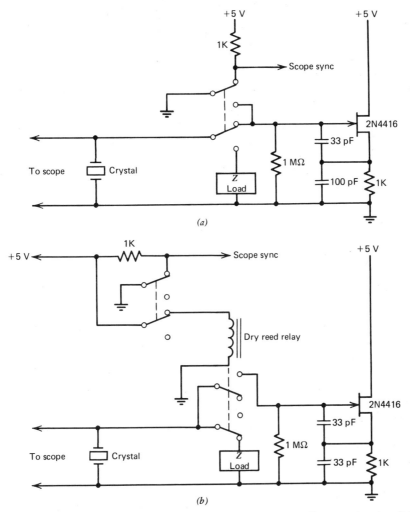

Figure 6.11. Test circuits for measuring crystal loading effects on in-circuit Q: (a) at 1 MHz and (b) at 10 MHz.

The test circuits used for measuring the effects of loading on crystal Q are given in Figs. 6.10 and 6.11. In the 10-MHz test circuit, a dry reed relay rather than a mechanical switch was used to switch the crystal, since the contact bounce time of a manually operated switch was excessive at this frequency.

CHAPTER SEVEN

ANALYSIS OF PHASE VERSUS FREQUENCY

For an oscillator to oscillate, the total phase shift around the oscillator loop has to be 0°, 360°, or some multiple of 360°. If the total phase shift around the loop changes slightly, the oscillation frequency moves up or down until the total phase shift is again back at 0°, 360°, or some multiple of 360°. The greater the rate of phase change with frequency, the less the frequency has to shift to drive the phase back to its null point. This correlates directly with circuit Q and the circuit's short-term frequency stability.

LC networks in the loop that are isolated from the crystal do not change phase with frequency fast enough to have any effect on short-term stability. LC networks directly connected to the crystal do have an effect on the rate of phase change with frequency, primarily because they can be used to short out or hide resistive sources and loads from the crystal.

In the following sections, various crystal circuit configurations and load conditions are analyzed for gain and phase changes with frequency. The intent is to maximize the phase change with frequency, since this is what gives short-term stability to an oscillator.

For brevity, derivations of gain and phase-shift equations for the circuits are not shown, and only analytical results are given. The circuit equations are derived as follows. Each circuit consists of one to three interconnected loops of RLC components. An equation is written for each loop, using standard circuit analysis techniques, and steady state conditions are assumed. These equations are then solved as a simultaneous set of linear equations for the circuits' gain and phase-shift transfer functions of $|E_0/E_i|$ and $E_0/E_i \angle\theta$ and plotted as a function of frequency. Since everything of interest happens near the crystal's series-resonant frequency, the plotted data curves are limited to frequencies near series resonance, with the frequency scale marked in parts-per-million (ppm) deviation from the crystal's series-resonant frequency.

The analysis has been simplified by ignoring the shunt capacitance C_0 across the crystal's case terminals, which limits the validity of the analysis to what happens near series resonance. The analytical curves shown were programmed and calculated on a TI-59 calculator. To help make comparisons between circuits, all phase and amplitude curves are plotted to the same scale, and the same 1-MHz crystal values are used in all the fundamental circuits. For the VHF harmonic circuits, the same 20-MHz third harmonic crystal values are used in all of those circuits.

7.1. RESISTIVE LOAD ON CRYSTAL

A circuit with a resistive load on the crystal is shown in Fig. 7.1, with typical circuit values listed. Figure 7.2 shows the circuit's phase shift (E_0/E_i) $\angle\theta$ as a function of frequency, and Fig. 7.3 shows the circuit's gain $|E_0/E_i|$ as a function of frequency. These curves are typical for a reasonably small resistive load on the crystal. Although not shown, if source and load resistances are increased, the rate of phase change with frequency decreases, indicating poorer short-term frequency stability. If source and load resistances are decreased, the rate of phase change with frequency increases, indicating better short-term frequency stability. The maximum phase change with frequency occurs with zero source and load resistances. Assuming no phase shift in the amplifier, this circuit will oscillate exactly at series resonance.

7.2. CAPACITIVE LOAD ON CRYSTAL

A circuit with a capacitive load on the crystal is shown in Fig. 7.4, with typical circuit values listed. Figure 7.2 shows the circuit's phase shift

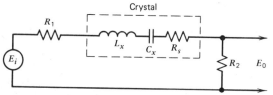

Figure 7.1.   Resistive load on crystal: Frequency = 1 MHz; L_x = 4.2 H; C_x = 0.006031228 pF; R_s = 240 Ω; R_1 = 120 Ω; R_2 = 120 Ω.

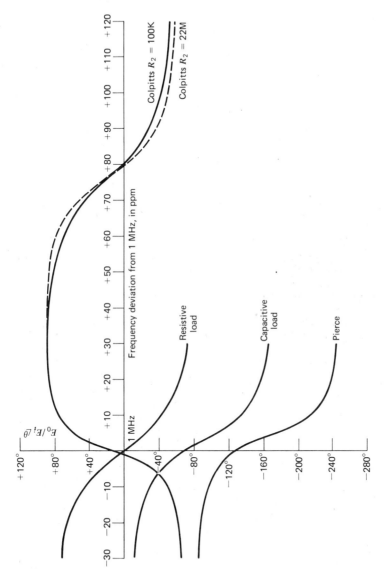

Figure 7.2. Phase shift versus frequency at 1 MHz.

81

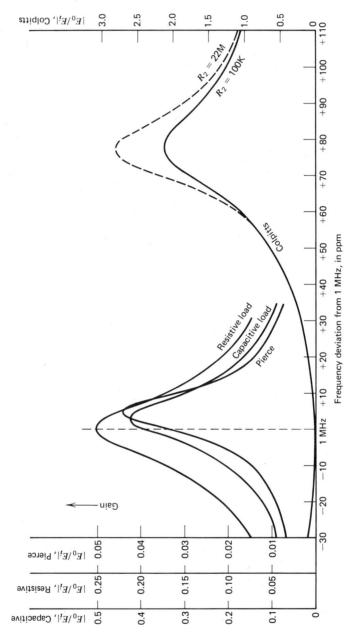

Figure 7.3. Gain versus frequency at 1 MHz.

82

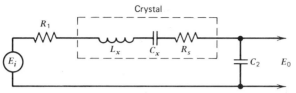

Figure 7.4. Capacitive load on crystal: Frequency = 1 MHz; L_x = 4.2 H; C_x = 0.0060310228 pF; R_s = 240 Ω; R_1 = 120 Ω; C_2 = 1000 pF.

(E_0/E_i) $\angle\theta$ with frequency, and Fig. 7.3 shows the circuit's gain $|E_0/E_i|$ versus frequency. Note that in Fig. 7.2 the phase slope is greater with a capacitive load than a resistive load on the crystal.

The general idea is to try to use these circuits where the phase slope is the steepest. With the capacitive load this occurs at 3 ppm above the 1-MHz series-resonance frequency. The phase shift through the network at this frequency is a 90° lag. Amplifiers usually have a phase shift of 0° or 180°. So if this capacitive load circuit is to be used in an oscillator, another 90° phase-shift network should be added to the circuit either to increase the phase shift to 180° or decrease it to 0°, depending on whether the amplifier is inverting or noninverting.

7.3. PIERCE CIRCUIT

A simplified Pierce circuit (without amplifier) is shown in Fig. 7.5. An explanation of how this circuit works is given in Section 5.8 and will not be repeated here. The phase shift of this circuit from input to output (E_0/E_i) $\angle\theta$ is shown in Fig. 7.2; the amplitude transfer function, or gain, $|E_0/E_i|$ is shown in Fig. 7.3. Figure 7.2 shows that if this circuit is used with a 180° inverting amplifier, it will oscillate about 6 ppm above series resonance.

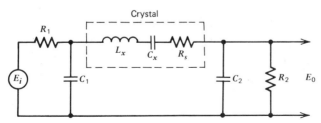

Figure 7.5. Simplified Pierce circuit: Frequency = 1 MHz; L_x = 4.2 H; C_x = 0.0060310228 pF; R_s = 240 Ω; R_1 = 1000 Ω; R_2 = 1000 Ω; C_1 = 0.001 μF; C_2 = 0.002 μF.

The phase slope is higher than either the resistive or capacitive load circuits in Fig. 7.2, indicating that it will have better short-term frequency stability than either of those circuits. Note that in Fig. 7.5 capacitors C_1 and C_2 tend to short out source and load resistances, raising the crystal's effective in-circuit Q. It is this shorting-out factor that gives the Pierce circuit its high phase slope with frequency and the very good frequency stability that goes with it.

7.4.   COLPITTS CIRCUIT

A simplified Colpitts circuit (without amplifier) is shown in Fig. 7.6. As mentioned in Section 5.3, the Colpitts has three different operating states: transistor on, transistor saturated, and transistor shut off. The longest of the three states occurs when the transistor is shut off, so the shut-off stage was picked as the most typical and is the one shown in Fig. 7.6. The phase shift (E_0/E_i) $\angle\theta$ of this circuit is shown in Fig. 7.2, and the amplitude transfer function, or gain, $|E_0/E_i|$ is shown in Fig. 7.3.

The solid curves in Figs. 7.2 and 7.3 represent a transistor-Colpitts, where the crystal's load resistor R_2 is the transistor's base bias resistor of 100K Ω. The dotted curves represent a FET-Colpitts circuit, where the crystal's load resistor R_2 is the FET's gate-to-ground resistor of 22 MΩ. The circuit's actual frequency stability is better than the low slope of the phase shift curve in Fig. 7.2 would indicate, which means that the transistor shut-off state shown in Fig. 7.6 is a poor average of the three states in the actual circuit. Improving the simplified circuit's accuracy requires including the other two states of operation. This requires a large effort. It

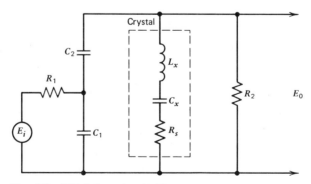

Figure 7.6.   Simplified Colpitts circuit: Frequency $= 1$ MHz; $L_x = 4.2$ H; $C_x = 0.0060310228$ pF; $R_s = 240\,\Omega$; $R_1 = 2\mathrm{K}\,\Omega$; $R_2 = 100\mathrm{K}\,\Omega$; $C_1 = 220$ pF; $C_2 = 47$ pF.

is necessary to match the boundary conditions of the three operating states and the results are not considered worth the effort.

However, the phase shift curve in Fig. 7.2 is correct in showing that the oscillation frequency is a high 79 ppm above series resonance (the actual oscillation frequency measured in the 1 MHz transistor-Colpitts circuit was 94 ppm above series resonance). Note that the phase shift curve in Fig. 7.2 shows 0° phase shift at two frequencies where oscillation could occur, but that the amplitude curve in Fig. 7.3 shows that only the higher frequency of 79 ppm above series resonance has enough gain (i.e., >1) for oscillation to occur.

7.5. MODIFIED MEACHAM CIRCUIT

The modified Meacham half bridge circuit is shown for analysis in Fig. 7.7. The coefficient P allows various bridge excitation ratios between the split-load phase inverter's emitter and collector voltages. When the bridge's excitation ratio P is changed, the bridge resistor PR_2 is changed proportionately with respect to the crystal's internal series resistance R_s in order to maintain bridge balance.

The emitter and collector source resistances R_1' and R_1 have different resistance values when measured independently with respect to ground. The two source resistances have the same resistance value, however, if measured with a load tied between them rather than from each point to ground. The source resistances are equal even if the phase inverter's emitter and collector resistors (R_1' and R_1) are not equal.

The capacitances shunting the two bridge arms are nominally bal-

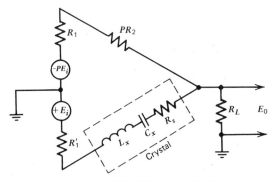

Figure 7.7.   Modified Meacham half-bridge circuit: Frequency = 1 MHz; L_x = 4.2 H; C_x = 0.0060310228 pF; R_s = 240 Ω; R_1 = 8 Ω; R_1' = 8 Ω; R_L = 2000 Ω; P = 1, 0.5, 0.25, 0.125; R_2 = 240, 480, 960, 1920 Ω.

anced to the bridge null. For simplicity, they are left out of the analysis, since they are primarily important for high-frequency stability reasons in this circuit and have little effect on oscillation frequency. The omission limits the accuracy of the analysis, but the intent here is to show only the general amplitude and phase characteristics of the bridge.

Figures 7.8 and 7.9 show the phase shift $(E_0/E_i) \angle \theta$ and gain $|E_0/E_i|$ of the modified Meacham half-bridge circuit for various amounts of bridge unbalance. Both bridge arms have equal excitation voltages ($P = 1$). The

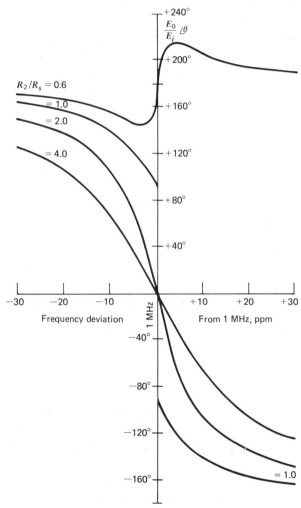

Figure 7.8. Bridge phase shift versus frequency for several amounts of imbalance from null. Bridge excitation ratio $P = 1$ for all curves.

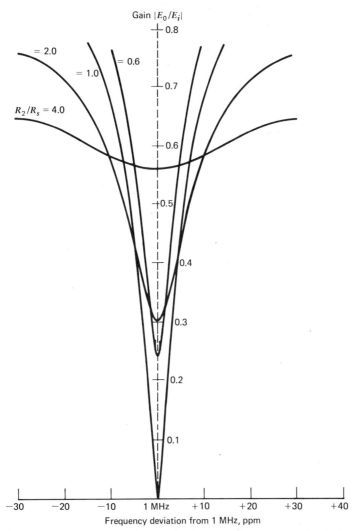

Figure 7.9. Bridge gain versus frequency for several amounts of imbalance from null. Bridge excitation ratio $P = 1$ for all curves.

only changes in the curves occur near the crystal's resonant frequency (1 MHz, in this case), so only the circuit's response at frequencies near resonance is shown. The curves are plotted in terms of the bridge-imbalance ratio R_2/R_s. When $R_2/R_s = 1$, the bridge is balanced with zero output from the bridge at resonance, as shown in Fig. 7.9. At frequencies away from resonance, the output amplitude approaches the input amplitude regardless of the amount of imbalance.

The phase shift through the bridge varies from $+180°$ at low frequencies to $0°$ at resonance to $-180°$ at high frequencies. The one exception to this phase characteristic is when the ratio R_2/R_s is less than one, and then the phase shift through the bridge stays near $+180°$ at all frequencies. The circuit will not oscillate (except parasitically) when R_2/R_s is equal to or less than one, so the useful phase curves are those with a ratio of R_2/R_s greater than one.

The steeper the slope of the phase shift curve in Fig. 7.8, the better the short-term frequency stability will be, since a smaller frequency change is then needed to provide any given amount of phase-angle correction and maintain the total phase shift around the oscillator loop at $0°$ (or $360°$). To provide a comparison, the Pierce circuit's phase shift (Fig. 7.2) falls about halfway between the two phase-shift curves $R_2/R_s = 2$ and $R_2/R_s = 4$ in Fig. 7.8 or at about $R_2/R_s = 3$. Thus, by operating the Meacham half-bridge with a R_2/R_s ratio of less than three, we should get a short-term stability better than that of the Pierce circuit. The Meacham circuit can be operated with a R_2/R_s ratio of less than three (a ratio of 1.0 is the theoretical limit) by the simple expedient of increasing the oscillator's amplifier gain. In practice, this is not so simple, since the tendency for parasitic oscillation increases when the gain is increased.

There are advantages to operating the Meacham half-bridge with unequal excitation voltages ($P \neq 1$) to the two bridge arms. In particular, it is advantageous for the excitation voltage driving the crystal to be larger than the voltage driving R_2. These advantages are described in detail in Section 5.11. Figures 7.10 and 7.11 show the bridge's phase shift (E_0/E_i $\angle\theta$ and gain $|E_0/E_i|$ functions for several values of P, the bridge excitation ratio.

All of the curves in Figs. 7.10 and 7.11 use the same bridge-imbalance ratio $R_2/R_s = 2$. This imbalance ratio is typical of the actual Meacham circuits described later in Chapters 10 and 11. The curves show that changing the excitation ratio does not change the phase curve much, but it does change the amplitude curve considerably, particularly at frequencies away from resonance. At frequencies away from resonance, the bridge's gain, or amplitude ratio, $|E_0/E_i|$ decreases in direct proportion as the excitation ratio P is decreased, which helps considerably in reducing parasitic oscillations.

The exact amount of bridge imbalance is slightly different in each of the four curves in Figs. 7.10 and 7.11, since the source resistances R_1 and R_1' do not change with P. The effect of the difference on the curves is relatively small. The biggest effect is a 16% reduction in the gain curves in Fig. 7.11 at the frequency of resonance (1 MHz).

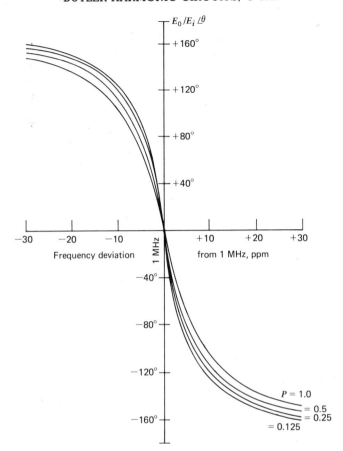

Figure 7.10. Bridge phase shift versus frequency for several values of bridge excitation ratio P. The bridge has a fixed null imbalance of $R_2/R_s = 2$ for all curves.

7.6. BUTLER HARMONIC CIRCUITS, C-TAP

The capacitive tap versions of Butler's emitter follower and common base oscillator circuits are shown in Figs. 7.12 and 7.13. These two circuits are analyzed together, since analytically they are the same circuit, one being the reverse of the other. The one difference between them is the gain $|E_0/E_i|$, which peaks at about 2.3 maximum for the emitter follower circuit and at about 0.035 maximum for the common base circuit. Phase shifts are the same, gain curve shapes are the same, and the crystal's source impedance Z_s in one circuit is the crystal's load impedance Z_L in the other. The notation of the emitter follower circuit will be used here for convenience, since its amplifier has a known gain of one with

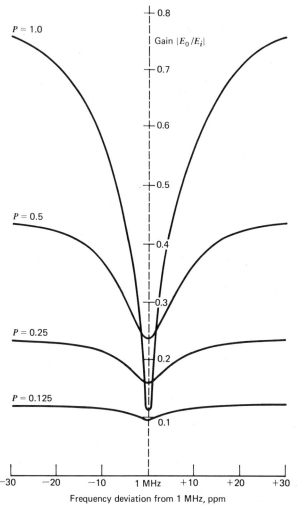

Figure 7.11. Bridge gain versus frequency for several values of bridge excitation ratio P. The bridge has a fixed null imbalance of $R_2/R_s = 2$ for all curves.

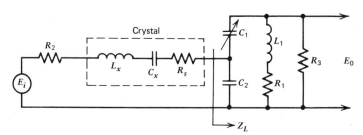

Figure 7.12. Butler emitter follower, capacitive tap.

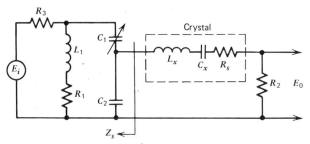

Figure 7.13. Butler common base, capacitive tap: Frequency = 20 MHz; L_x = 0.053 H; C_x = 0.0011948253 pF; R_s = 30 Ω; R_1 = 0.02–0.45 Ω; R_2 = 15 Ω; R_3 = 1000 Ω; C_1 = 12–448 pF; C_2 = 150, 330, 680 pF; L_1 = 0.25–4.0 μH.

zero phase shift, which makes the gain and phase curves easier to understand and interpret. The oscillation frequency used is 20 MHz, since this is the lowest frequency that this circuit is likely to be used at.

The crystal's load impedance is primarily determined by C_2. C_2 is normally selected so that its impedance is approximately equal to or a little less than the crystal's internal series resistance R_s. For analysis purposes, three values of C_2 are selected—one whose impedance is lower than R_s, one approximately equal to R_s, and one higher than R_s. For each value of C_2, three values of L_1 are selected, with the middle value of L_1 in each case selected to give near maximum circuit gain. This gives nine sets of data, which are sufficient to show the effects of the different circuit components. These nine data sets are plotted in Figs. 7.14, 7.15, and 7.16 and show the following results:

1. Circuit loop gain varies with frequency, L_1, and C_1. For any given value of C_2, there is an optimum value of C_1 for maximum circuit gain. Maximum circuit gain occurs when L_1 is selected to give a C_2/C_1 ratio of about 4.

2. Oscillation is generally slightly *above* series resonance but can be set exactly *at* series resonance by tuning C_1 to the right value.

3. The impedance of C_2 must be equal to or less than the crystal's internal series resistance R_s if the crystal's load impedance is to be kept reasonably small.

4. The frequency of oscillation is relatively insensitive to the value of C_2. Making C_2 smaller moves the oscillation band slowly upward and farther away from series resonance.

5. Slopes of the better phase shift versus frequency curves are reasonably high, indicating that good short-term frequency stability can be obtained by selecting the right component values.

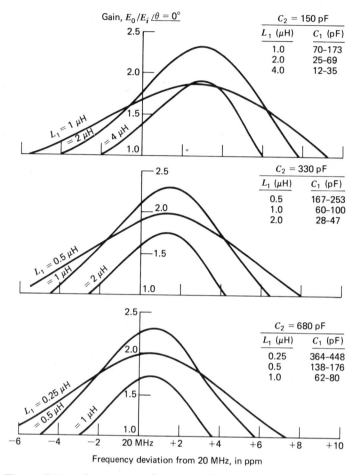

Figure 7.14.   Gain versus frequency for Butler circuits, C-tap.

All five of these analytical results have been observed experimentally in the test circuits. It may be helpful to explain how data in Figs. 7.14, 7.15, and 7.16 were calculated. Oscillation occurs at that frequency where the phase shift through the network is zero. For a given set of circuit values, the frequency of zero phase shift (i.e., the frequency of oscillation) is varied by tuning C_1 over a range of values. The gain through the circuit at each frequency of zero phase shift (E_0/E_i) $\angle\theta = 0°$ is plotted in Fig. 7.14 as a function of the oscillation frequency. The crystal's load impedance $|Z_L|$ is plotted in Fig. 7.16 as a function of the oscillation frequency, under the same condition of zero phase shift through the circuit.

For the plots of phase shift (E_0/E_i) $\angle\theta$ versus frequency in Fig. 7.15, values of all circuit components including C_1 are held fixed, since we are interested here in how large a phase-angle correction is generated if the

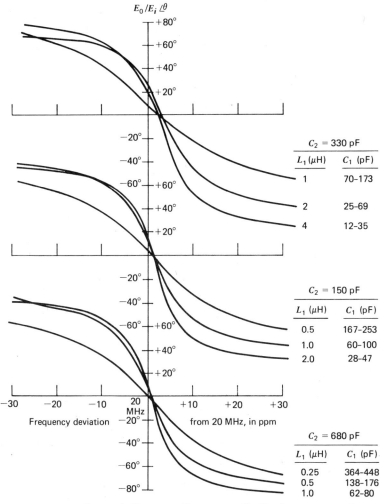

Figure 7.15. Phase shift versus frequency for Butler circuits, C-tap.

oscillation frequency were to deviate slightly from the frequency of zero phase shift. The frequencies at which the phase shifts were calculated were at the peaks of the gain curves shown in Fig. 7.14. Any part of the gain curves in Fig. 7.14 could have been used, however, since phase-shift calculations at other frequencies across the gain curves all showed the same rate of phase change with frequency.

7.7. BUTLER HARMONIC CIRCUITS, L-TAP

Inductive tap versions of Butler's emitter follower and common base amplifier circuits are shown in Figs. 7.17 and 7.18. The two circuits are

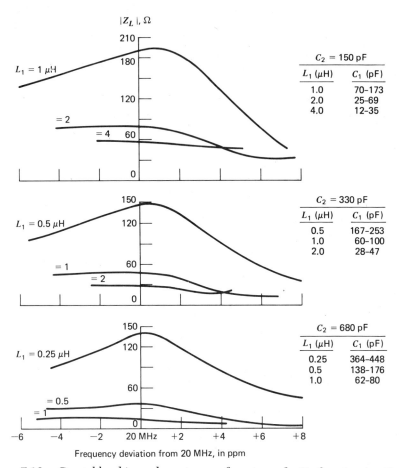

Figure 7.16. Crystal load impedance versus frequency for Butler circuits, C-tap.

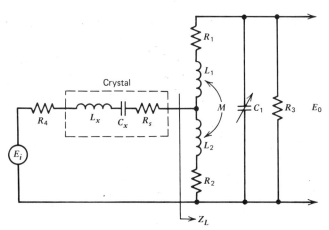

Figure 7.17. Butler emitter follower, inductive tap.

94

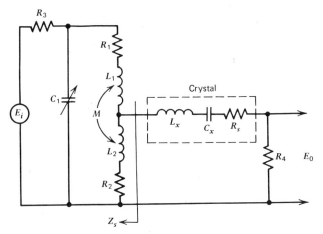

Figure 7.18. Butler common base, inductive tap: Frequency = 20 MHz; L_x = 0.053 H; C_x = 0.0011948253 pF; R_s = 30 Ω; R_1 = 0.01–0.41 Ω; R_2 = 0.004–0.036 Ω; R_3 = 1000 Ω; R_4 = 15 Ω; C_1 = 7–270 pF; K = $M/\sqrt{L_1 L_2}$ = 0.12; L_1 = 0.14–3.45 μ H; L_2 = 0.08, 0.15, 0.30 μ H; M = .013–0.122 μ H; L_{total} = $L_1 + L_2 + 2M$ = 0.25–4.0 μH.

analyzed together, since analytically they are the same circuit, one being the reverse of the other. The one difference between them is the gain $|E_0/E_i|$, which peaks at about 2.3 maximum for the emitter follower circuit and at about 0.035 maximum for the common base circuit. Phase shifts are the same, gain curves are the same, and the crystal's source impedance Z_s in one circuit is the crystal's load impedance Z_L in the other. The notation of the emitter follower circuit will be used here, since its amplifier has a known gain of one with zero phase shift, which makes the calculated gain and phase curves easier to understand and interpret. The oscillation frequency used is 20 MHz, since this is the lowest frequency at which this circuit is likely to be used.

The crystal's load impedance is primarily determined by L_2, the inductance of the tapped portion of the inductor, as shown in Figs. 7.17 and 7.18. Normally, L_2 is selected so that its impedance is approximately equal to or a little less than the crystal's internal series resistance R_s. For analysis purposes, three values of L_2 are selected, whose impedances are lower than R_s, approximately equal to R_s, and higher than R_s. And for each value of L_2, three inductance values for the whole inductor L_{total} are selected, with the middle value selected in each case to give near maximum circuit gain. This gives nine sets of data, which are sufficient to show the effects of different circuit components. The single-layer air-core Miller coils used in the test circuits had an average coefficient of

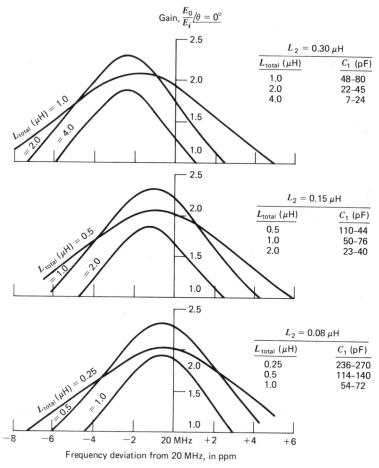

Figure 7.19. Gain versus frequency for Butler circuits, L-tap.

coupling K ($K = M/\sqrt{L_1 L_2}$) of 0.12. This coefficient was used to specify mutual inductance M between the two parts of the solenoid coil L_1 and L_2.

Analytical data are plotted in Figs. 7.19, 7.20, and 7.21 and show the following results:

1. Circuit gain varies with frequency, L_1, and C_1. For any given value of L_2, there is an optimum value of L_1 for maximum circuit gain. Maximum circuit gain occurs when the crystal is tapped into the coil at about ⅙ of the coil's total number of turns.

2. Oscillation is generally *below* series resonance but can be set exactly *at* series resonance by tuning C_1.

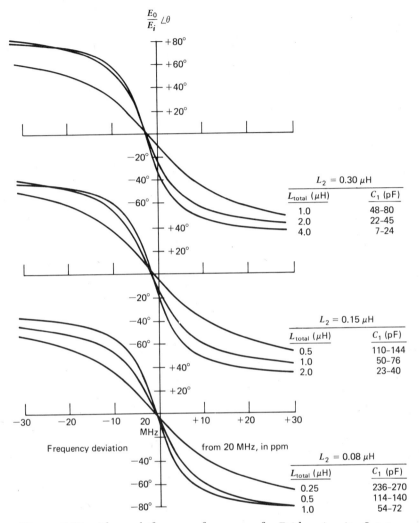

Figure 7.20. Phase shift versus frequency for Butler circuits, L-tap.

3. The impedance of L_2 must be equal to or less than the crystal's internal series resistance R_s if the crystal's load impedance is to be kept reasonably small.

4. Frequency of oscillation is relatively insensitive to the value of L_2. Making L_2 larger moves the oscillation band slowly downward and farther away from series resonance.

5. Slopes of the better curves of phase shift versus frequency are reasonably high, indicating that good short-term frequency stability can be had by selecting the right component values.

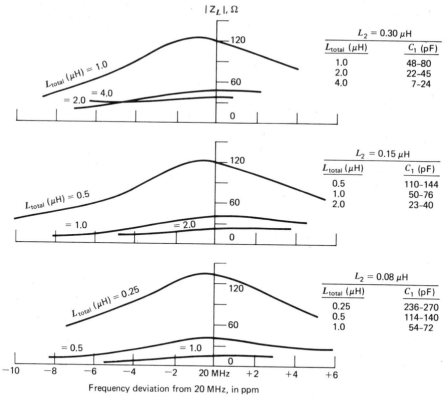

Figure 7.21. Crystal load impedance versus frequency for Butler circuits, L-tap.

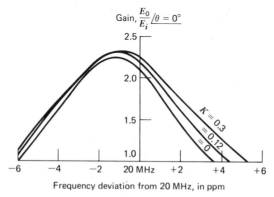

Figure 7.22. Gain versus frequency for Butler circuits, L-tap, as a function of the coil's mutual coupling coefficient K. $L_1 = 0.7686\ \mu H$, $L_2 = 0.15\ \mu H$.

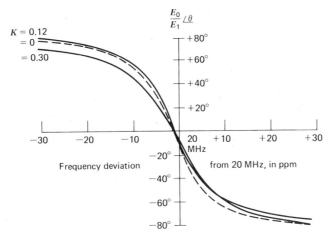

Figure 7.23. Phase shift versus frequency for Butler circuits, L-tap, as a function of the coil's mutual coupling coefficient K. $L_1 = 0.7686\,\mu H$, $L_2 = 0.15\,\mu H$.

6. Maximum gain is about 2.4 peak for the Butler emitter follower circuit. And although it is not shown in the figures, maximum gain for the Butler common base circuit was calculated as 0.035 peak.

The curves in Figs. 7.19, 7.20, and 7.21 were calculated the same way as curves in Figs. 7.14, 7.15, and 7.16. The reader is referred to Section 7.6 for an explanation of how these curves were calculated.

All six of the analytical results have been observed experimentally in test circuits, with one important difference. The inductive tap circuit would oscillate only below and not at series resonance. In the test circuits, gain curves in Fig. 7.19 appeared to be shifted about 5 ppm farther down in frequency. The Butler emitter follower circuit (but not the Butler common base circuit) could be made to oscillate at series resonance or slightly above it, just as Fig. 7.19 shows, by removing the diode amplitude clamp across the coil. Why this happens is not understood.

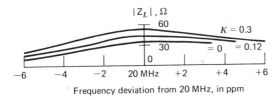

Figure 7.24. Crystal load impedance versus frequency for Butler circuits, L-tap, as a function of the coil's mutual coupling coefficient K. $L_1 = 0.7686\,\mu H$, $L_2 = 0.15\,\mu H$.

The inductive tap circuit differs from the capacitive tap circuit in that it has mutual coupling between the two tapped portions of the coil. Does the mutual coupling have any effect on the circuit? Not much, it turns out. The maximum practical value of the coefficient of coupling K for a single-layer tapped solenoid is about 0.3. Figures 7.22, 7.23, and 7.24 show calculated values of circuit gain, phase shift with frequency, and crystal load impedance for three values of K (0, 0.12, and 0.30), while leaving the values of L_1 and L_2 constant. As can be seen from the curves, the slope of the circuit's phase shift with frequency, the gain, and frequency of oscillation change very little when K changes. Only the crystal's load impedance changes significantly, increasing about 50% over the full range of K from 0 to 0.3.

The effect of mutual inductance on the circuit was checked in test circuits by breaking the tapped coil into two separate inductors oriented at 90° for minimum coupling ($K = 0$). The peak of the oscillation band did not shift, staying at about 5 ppm below series resonance, and the oscillation frequency stayed below series resonance.

CHAPTER EIGHT

TRIMMING THE CRYSTAL FREQUENCY

A certain amount of ± frequency tolerance must be allowed in manufacturing crystals to a specific frequency. In addition, either a reactive load on the crystal or a phase shift in the oscillator's amplifier will move the actual oscillation frequency slightly up or down from the crystal's own internal series-resonant value. To tune a crystal oscillator to a specific frequency, it is necessary to adjust the phase shift somewhere in the amplifier loop. This can be done by inserting either a variable inductor or a variable capacitor in the circuit, or by varying the resistance in an already existing RC or RL phase-shifting network. To raise the frequency, a phase lead is added to the amplifier loop, or an existing phase lag is decreased. To lower the frequency, a phase lag is added to the amplifier loop, or an existing phase lag is increased. In a harmonic oscillator, the frequency can be trimmed both up and down by varying the tuning of the circuit's LC tank.

The most common method of frequency trimming is putting a variable capacitor either in series or in parallel with the crystal. Figure 8.1 shows a variety of resistive and capacitive trimmer locations for three popular oscillator circuits. Table 8.1 shows the relative frequency sensitivity of most of these locations. Using an inductor rather than a capacitor will reverse the direction of frequency shift.

Placing a capacitor or an inductor directly in parallel with the crystal for frequency trimming purposes is not recommended, since it tends to short out the crystal and reduce the crystal's control over the circuit. Frequency trimming capacitors or inductors are not used in oscillator circuits in this book for reasons of simplicity and to make the circuits easier to understand.

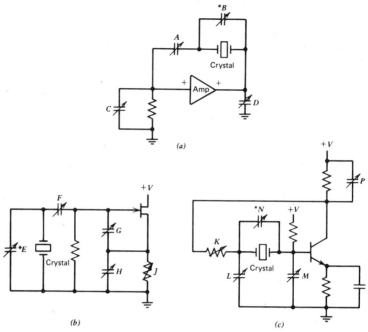

Figure 8.1. Capacitor locations for frequency trimming in three popular oscillator circuits. *Indicates locations that are not recommended. (a) Series resonant,
(b) Colpitts, and (c) Pierce.

TABLE 8.1
Relative Frequency Sensitivity of Various Condenser Trimmer Locations at 1 MHz

Circuit	Capacitance or Resistance Added	At Circuit Location[a] in Fig. 8.1 Marked	Frequency Change at 1 MHz (in ppm)
Series resonant	+33 pF	A	+120.
Series resonant	+33 pF	*B	−0.9
Series resonant	+33 pF	C	−0.3
Series resonant	+33 pF	D	−0.3
Colpitts	+33 pF	*E	−89.
Colpitts	+33 pF	F	+103.
Colpitts	+3 pF (10% of G)	G	−30.
Colpitts	+15 pF (10% of H)	H	−3.
Colpitts	+ΔR(10% of J)	J	−ΔF
Pierce	+ΔR(10% of K)	K	−ΔF
Pierce	+100 pF (10% of L)	L	−6.
Pierce	+100 pF (10% of M)	M	−0.3
Pierce	+15 pF	*N	+0.1
Pierce	+15 pF	P	−0.3

[a] The * indicates locations that are not recommended.

CHAPTER NINE

THE START-UP PROBLEM

Normally, when power is applied to an oscillator, we expect it to start oscillating. Unfortunately, it does not always start unless positive steps are taken to make sure it does. The key is DC biasing, and the solution is a little different for discrete transistors than for integrated circuits. The first section of this chapter covers biasing ICs, while the second covers biasing discrete transistors.

9.1. BIASING ICs

The amplifiers used in most of the IC oscillator circuits in this book are digital amplifiers: logic inverters, line receivers, voltage comparators, and so forth. They are designed to be used in either a "0" or "1" state. In either state, the amplifier is saturated, and the gain is zero. For oscillation to occur, a circuit's loop gain must be greater than one. Once oscillation starts, energy storage in the crystal will carry the oscillator through the saturated zero-gain intervals. Loop gain exceeds one only during switching intervals between binary states, closing the loop over part of each cycle. When power is first applied to a digital circuit, however, there is no energy storage in the crystal. And if the amplifier is in either binary state, loop gain is zero, and oscillation will not start.

The key to the start-up problem is selecting digital amplifiers to which negative feedback can be applied, in order to bias the amplifier's input and output terminals in the middle of their transition zones between the zero and one states, where the digital amplifier has a finite gain. Since negative feedback is needed only for DC biasing conditions, a shunt capacitance to ground can be added after the feedback resistor to (1) provide a 6-dB/octave frequency roll-off that will ensure a stable feedback amplifier condition and (2) limit the gain-reducing effects of the negative feedback network to low frequencies. The negative feedback network ensures that oscillation will always start when power is applied.

For an example, refer to the oscillator circuit in Fig. 9.1. This oscillator uses a voltage comparator as an amplifier. The voltage comparator is assumed to be a TTL unit with an output swing between 0 V and +5 VDC. The midpoint of the two resistors R_1 and R_1 provides a +2.5 VDC reference point halfway between binary zero and one output states. The positive (+) amplifier input terminal is tied to this DC reference point by R_2, and the comparator output will tend to follow this input toward one or the other of its two binary states. R_3 provides negative feedback from the amplifier output to the negative (−) input terminal of the amplifier in order to force the output voltage to follow the input voltage, and it stabilizes at +2.5 VDC. Capacitor C_1 limits negative feedback to low frequencies and together with R_3, provides a 6-dB/octave roll-off, which gives an inherently stable feedback amplifier condition. Both amplifier input and output are then in an unsaturated state, being biased in the middle of the transition zone, and the gain through the comparator amplifier is then greater than zero. All IC oscillators in this book use the negative feedback concept to ensure oscillation at start-up.

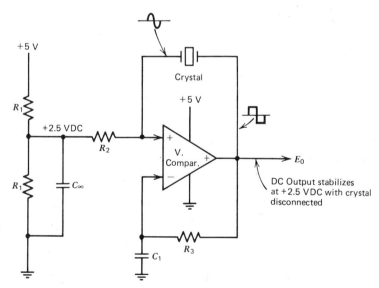

Figure 9.1.　Solving the start-up problem with negative feedback.

9.2. BIASING DISCRETE TRANSISTORS

Just as with an IC oscillator, a discrete transistor oscillator must be biased within its linear region if it is to start oscillating when power is applied. It is preferable to bias the transistor stage near the middle of its linear region, which means adjusting the bias so that the collector's DC output voltage is held halfway between ground and the power supply voltage. Figure 9.2 shows an assortment of DC biasing methods for a common emitter pulse-amplifier stage. These biasing circuits illustrate the tradeoff between circuit complexity and bias stability. The first three use a passive biasing arrangement, the second three use an active constant-current arrangement, and the last one uses an active voltage-feedback circuit. A short description of each configuration follows.

The simplest biasing arrangement is shown in Fig. 9.2a and is useful only at low and medium frequencies in a benign environment. There is no correction in this circuit for gain changes with temperature, and an adjustable resistor R_3 is required to handle gain differences between individual transistors. The collector's output voltage changes considerably if the power supply voltage changes by even a small amount. The circuit does not work well at high frequencies because it does not have a base-to-emitter discharge resistor R_2, as shown in Fig. 9.2b. This resistor R_2 is required for fast discharge of the transistor's base-to-emitter junction capacitance.

Figure 9.2b shows a biasing method that works a little better. Negative DC feedback from the collector is used to bias the transistor's base. Depending on the value of R_2, negative feedback will hold the collector's output voltage somewhere between a constant voltage and half the supply voltage, over a reasonably large supply-voltage change. Gain changes with temperature are partially corrected for. An adjustable biasing resistor R_3 is required to handle gain differences between individual transistors. This circuit will work at high frequencies because it has a base-to-emitter resistor R_2 for fast discharging of the transistor's base-to-emitter capacitance.

The biasing arrangement shown in Fig. 9.2c is widely used because it does not require an adjustable resistor. The collector's output voltage holds reasonably close to half the power supply voltage, with large changes in the power supply voltage and gain changes with temperature reasonably well-corrected for. The key to biasing this circuit is holding the base at a constant bias voltage (with a fixed power supply voltage) over the three to one differences in emitter current between individual transistors. An emitter resistor R_4 is required and used as an emitter cur-

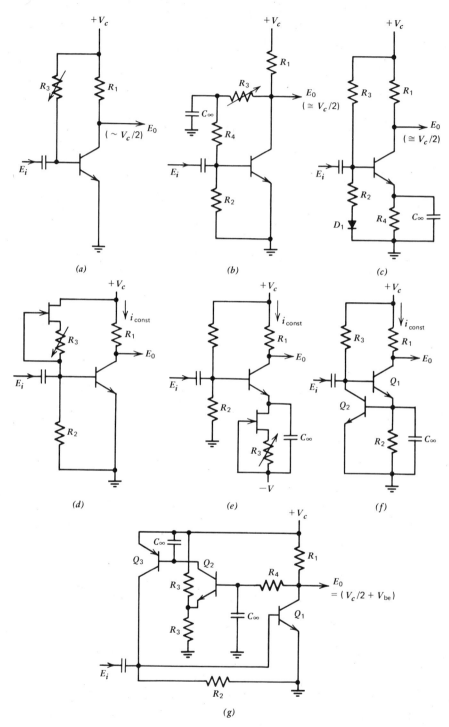

Figure 9.2(a–g). Some DC biasing schemes for a common emitter pulse amplifier stage.

rent feedback resistor. R_4 is selected to be a reasonably large percentage of the collector resistor R_1. The biasing resistors R_2 and R_3 are given medium resistance values, so that the usual 3 to 1 variation in the base biasing current between individual transistors does not shift the base biasing voltage significantly. Diode D_1 compensates for the transistor's base-to-emitter voltage drop. The diode is sometimes omitted in order to reduce circuit complexity. A fair amount of calculation is required to design this circuit, using maximum and minimum transistor gains and gain changes with temperature.

Figure 9.2d uses a FET to provide constant biasing current into the transistor's base. Depending on the value of R_2, the collector's output voltage is held somewhere between a constant voltage and a fixed voltage increment below the power supply voltage. Gain changes with temperature are not corrected for. An adjustable biasing resistor R_3 is required to compensate for pinch-off voltage differences between individual FETs and gain differences between individual transistors.

Figure 9.2e is useful if a negative supply voltage is available. It operates the same as Fig. 9.2d except that gain differences between individual transistors and transistor gain changes with temperature are corrected for. FET gain changes with temperature can be compensated for by adjusting current through the FET to its temperature null value. An adjustable biasing resistor R_3 is required to handle pinch-off voltage variations between individual FETs.

Figure 9.2f uses an emitter resistor R_2 to sample the emitter current of Q_1. Q_2 varies bias voltage on Q_1 to maintain a constant emitter current in Q_1. Q_1's collector output voltage is maintained at a fixed voltage increment below the power supply voltage. Gain changes with temperature are partially compensated for.

The best biasing scheme is also the most complex one, and it is shown in Fig. 9.2g. Figure 9.2g uses two transistors in a voltage-feedback scheme from the collector to the base of Q_1. It maintains the collector of Q_1 at one-half the supply voltage plus one V_{be} (base to emitter voltage, about 0.4 V). Transistor Q_2 measures the voltage difference between the collector of Q_1 and the center point of the two resistors R_3 and R_3, which is amplified and fed back to the base of Q_1. Q_1's collector voltage holds quite accurately at half the supply voltage plus one V_{be} because of the gain in the feedback loop. Gain changes with temperature in all of the transistors are corrected for, and no adjustable resistor is required.

CHAPTER TEN

DISCRETE TRANSISTOR OSCILLATORS

This chapter contains performance test data on the discrete transistor oscillator circuits described in Chapter 5. It is divided into three parts: The first describes the circuit selection and testing philosophy used; the second part describes individual fundamental oscillator circuits one by one; and the third describes individual harmonic oscillator circuits.

A. CIRCUIT SELECTION AND TESTING

The basic approach in selecting discrete transistor circuits was first to try all basic circuit types, then build a test circuit of each type to determine its strong and weak points. A total of 22 fundamental and 12 harmonic discrete transistor circuits were evaluated in this way. Where practical, the fundamental circuits were all tested at the same frequency of 1 MHz for comparison purposes, and the more important ones were also tested at the frequency extremes of 4 kHz and 20 MHz.

The harmonic circuits were tested at three frequencies: 20, 50, and 100 MHz. Except for special cases, 20 MHz is the lowest frequency at which a harmonic circuit would be used, and 100 MHz is near the upper 200-MHz harmonic frequency limit. 50 MHz was picked as near the middle of the harmonic frequency band.

After selection, each test circuit was individually optimized for best component values, bias, waveforms, and so forth. Because the transistors used have a strong effect on circuit performance, considerable time was spent selecting the right ones for each circuit. Many discrete transistor circuits are not compatible with digital logic, so level shifters or buffers were added to some of them to make them TTL compatible.

Photographs were taken of oscillator waveforms at various points in the circuits. The waveform photos of each circuit have been synchronized to a common point in time and vertically aligned together on the printed page to permit vertical phase comparisons between various parts of each circuit. To facilitate comparing the circuits with one other, the same crystals were used in all circuits, moving them from circuit to circuit as needed. The crystal most used is a 1-MHz crystal. It is an AT cut with an internal series resistance of 240 Ω and is solder sealed in a gas-filled HC-6 metal can.

The circuits were tested for frequency sensitivity to supply voltage and temperature variations. Sensitivity to supply voltage is checked by measuring the frequency shift when the power supply voltage is changed from +4 to +6 VDC. Since the object of the temperature testing was to measure temperature characteristics of the oscillator circuit itself and not the crystal, only the oscillator circuit was subjected to temperature changes, with the crystal left at room temperature. Temperature changes were obtained by the rather crude method of spraying the circuits (but not the crystal) with freon from an aerosol can for 10 seconds to cool the circuits, and blowing hot air on the circuits (but not on the crystal) with a heat gun for 20 seconds to heat the circuits. The temperature sensitivity numbers given in Tables 12.1, 12.2, and 12.3 are the changes in oscillator frequency when the circuit was heated or cooled in this fashion. The intention was to get a rough rather than accurate measure of the circuits' sensitivity to these effects.

The short-term frequency stability of some of the oscillator circuits was checked by measuring the frequency with a frequency counter and looking at the variation in frequency over a short 20–40 second time interval. Measured this way, short-term stability contains errors due to the $\pm$ 1 count accuracy of the counter and inherent short-term frequency variations in the counter's internal oscillator. The intent, again, was to get a rough rather than accurate measure of the short-term stability of the different circuits.

Because temperature and short-term stability measurements were not very accurate, no attention should be paid to small differences in these numbers among circuits. Only a reasonably large difference has any significance.

No long-term frequency stability measurements were made on any oscillator circuits. There are several reasons for this. First, the stability needs of most digital circuitry can be satisfied with much less than the maximum stability obtainable from a crystal oscillator. Second, to be meaningful, any long-term stability measurements would have to be made over a protracted period of time. And third, even if such data were obtained, it would be difficult to sort out what was due to the circuit from what was due to the crystal.

B. FUNDAMENTAL CIRCUITS

10.1. MILLER-FET

The schematic of this oscillator at 1 MHz is shown in Fig. 10.1a. The crystal operates as a shunt element in this circuit and requires a high load resistance to operate properly. A FET has a high input resistance and makes an ideal amplifier here. The parallel L_1C_1 network is not at resonance and must have a net inductive impedance for oscillation to occur. Although C_1 is not necessary for oscillation to occur, the photographs in Figs. 10.1b and c show how much C_1 cleans up the waveform across L_1. With $C_1 = 470$ pF, the waveform across the crystal improves to a very nice sine wave and increases considerably in amplitude. The oscillation frequency is very sensitive to C_2 and the drain-to-gate capacitance in parallel with C_2. Because the effective value of C_2 is C_2 multiplied by the amplifier gain (the Miller effect), the frequency changes significantly when the FET is changed or when the stage gain changes with power supply or temperature changes. Because of this, the Miller circuit is not a very stable oscillator.

10.2. MILLER-TRANSISTOR

The schematic of this oscillator at 1 MHz is shown in Fig. 10.2a. The purpose of this circuit is to show the heavy crystal loading that occurs if a bipolar transistor is used for the amplifier instead of a FET. The parallel L_1C_1 network must have a net inductive impedance for oscillation to occur. Although C_1 is not necessary for oscillation to occur, waveform photographs in Figs. 10.2b and c show how much C_1 cleans up waveforms across both L_1 and the crystal. The crystal waveform in Fig. 10.2c is still very poor even with $C_1 = 470$ pF and shows that using a bipolar transistor rather than a FET gives a much poorer oscillator.

The oscillation frequency is very sensitive to C_2 and the transistor's

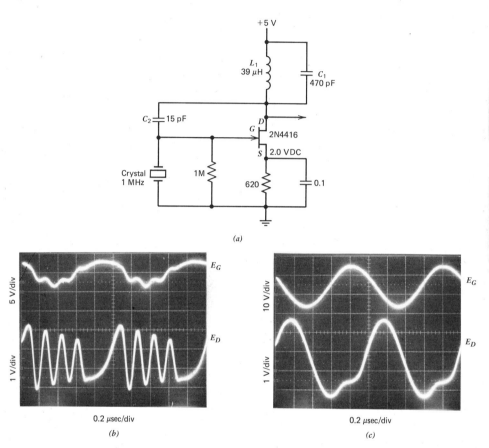

Figure 10.1. Miller-FET at (a) 1 MHz, (b) $C_1 = 0$, and (c) $C_1 = 470$ pF.

collector-to-base capacitance in parallel with C_2. Because the effective value of C_2 is C_2 multiplied by the amplifier gain (Miller effect), frequency changes significantly when the transistor is changed or when the amplifier gain changes with power supply or temperature changes. Because of this, the Miller circuit is not a stable oscillator.

10.3. COLPITTS-FET

A schematic of this circuit at 1 MHz is shown in Fig. 10.3a. The Colpitts is a parallel resonant circuit and requires a high shunt-load impedance on the crystal. A FET amplifier, with its high input impedance, is a good

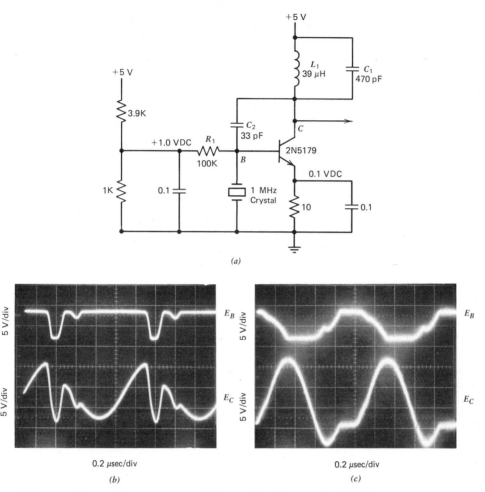

Figure 10.2. Miller-transistor at (a) 1 MHz, (b) $C_1 = 0$, and (c) $C_1 = 470$ pF.

selection for the Colpitts oscillator. The voltage swing on the crystal is rather large, from +6 to −6 VDC. The waveform at the FET's source shows three operating modes over a cycle: conduction on a rising wavefront, saturation limiting at the positive peak, and FET cutoff and RC exponential decay on a falling wavefront. The circuit has a good short-term stability of ± 0.1 ppm.

When the frequency is changed, the time constant R_1C_1 must be changed. In the FET version, it is convenient to leave R_1 fixed (to hold the drain current constant) and vary C_1.

What happens when the resistor R_1 is replaced with an inductor? Figure 10.3b shows the same circuit with the 2.4K Ω emitter resistor R_1 re-

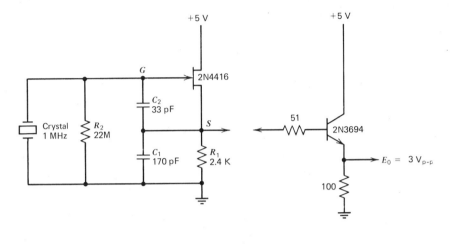

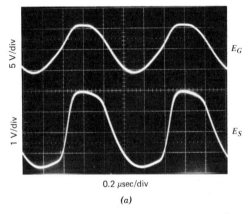

Figure 10.3(a). Colpitts-FET at 1 MHz. R_2 must be $\geq$ 1 MΩ for no loading effects and $\geq$ 22K Ω for oscillation to occur.

placed with a 550-μH inductor. The inductor's 3000-Ω reactance at 1 MHz is a little higher than the 2400 Ω of resistor R_1, but it is close enough. Note the much larger waveform amplitudes in Fig. 10.3b when the inductor is used, so much so that the FET's gate goes above +5 VDC and acts as a diode clamp through the FET's drain to the +5 V power supply.

The circuit in Fig. 10.3b is more important as a harmonic oscillator than as a fundamental one, but it is included here for waveform comparison with Fig. 10.3a. The larger voltage swing across the crystal shows that the in-circuit Q is much higher with the inductor L_1 rather than the resistor R_1 in the circuit.

A schematic for operation at 4 kHz is shown in Fig. 10.3c. Note the

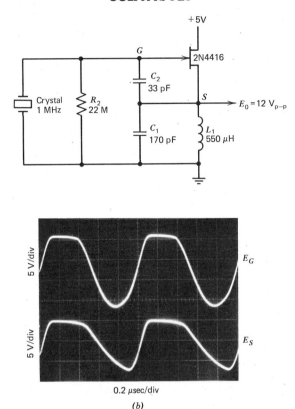

Figure 10.3(*b*).   Colpitts-FET at 1 MHz, using an inductor L_1 instead of resistor R_1 in Fig. 10.3*a*. $L_1 C_1$ is *not* tuned to resonance.

very high shunt resistance required across the crystal to operate at 4 kHz. A FET is the obvious choice for the amplifier in this circuit because of its high input resistance.

A schematic for operation at 10 MHz is shown in Fig. 10.3*d*. At these higher frequencies, the J309 FET works better than the 2N4416, because it has twice the transconductance of the 2N4416 and half the output resistance. The output resistance must be low to drive the low impedance of C_1 at high frequencies. The J309 requires twice the drain current, so R_1 is cut in half to provide this. C_1 is then doubled to keep the $R_1 C_1$ time constant the same.

10 MHz is about the upper limit for a FET-Colpitts circuit. Above 10 MHz, a bipolar transistor makes a better amplifier choice. The output resistance of a transistor emitter follower is 5 to 10 times lower than that of a FET source follower, which makes it much easier for the transistor to drive the lower circuit impedance of a high-frequency oscillator circuit.

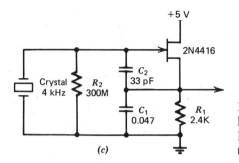

(c)

Figure 10.3(c). Colpitts-FET at 4 kHz. R_2 must be $\geq$ 220 MΩ for no loading effects and $\geq$ 5 MΩ for oscillation to occur.

And the low crystal impedance at these higher frequencies makes the medium input resistance of a transistor amplifier more acceptable as a load for the crystal.

10.4. COLPITTS-TRANSISTOR

A schematic of this circuit at 1 MHz is shown in Fig. 10.4a. The voltage swing across the crystal is rather large, from +5 to −1 VDC. The waveform at the transistor's emitter shows three operating modes over a cycle: normal transistor operation over a short interval near the end of the rising crystal waveform, transistor saturation at the positive signal peak, and transistor shut-off and a long RC exponential decay with a falling crystal waveform. The circuit has a good short-term stability of ± 0.1 ppm.

To change frequency, the time constant R_1C_1 must be changed. In the transistor version of the Colpitts, it is convenient to change R_1 and leave C_1 fixed. This increases the transistor's input resistance as the frequency goes lower, where the crystal's load resistance must be higher. It also

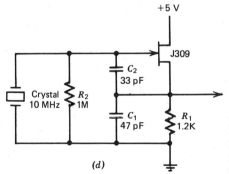

(d)

Figure 10.3(d). Colpitts-FET at 10 MHz. R_2 must be $\geq$ 100K Ω for no loading effects and $\geq$ 3.3K Ω for oscillation to occur.

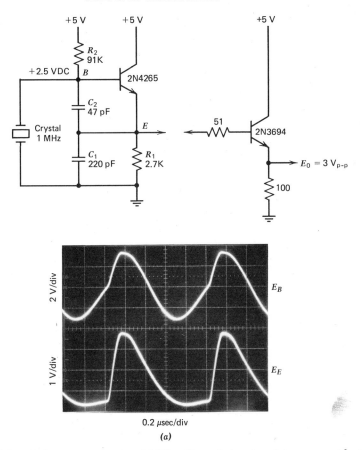

Figure 10.4(a). Colpitts-transistor at 1 MHz. Crystal shunt resistance must be ≥ 1 MΩ for no loading effects and ≥ 22K Ω for oscillation to occur.

helps to use a high-gain transistor to get the highest possible input resistance at the transistor's base input terminal and minimize crystal loading by the transistor.

What happens when the resistor R_1 is replaced with an inductor? Figure 10.4b shows the same circuit as Fig. 10.4a but with the 2.7K Ω emitter resistor R_1 replaced with a 550-μH inductance L_1. Its reactive impedance is 3.1K Ω at 1 MHz, roughly near the 2.4K Ω of R_1. The bias resistor R_2 is increased to 470K Ω to compensate for removing the emitter resistor R_1. The waveforms show an increased Q, with signal voltages almost three times larger in amplitude and the peaks showing stronger clipping. This circuit is more important as a harmonic oscillator than as a fundamental one, but it is included here for waveform comparison with Fig. 10.4a.

A schematic for operation at 200 kHz is shown in Fig. 10.4c. 200 kHz

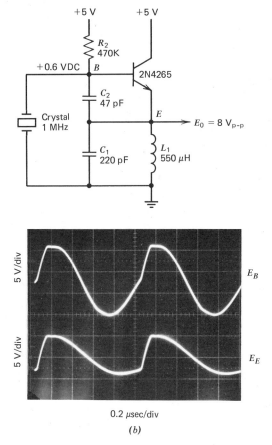

Figure 10.4(b). Colpitts-transistor at 1 MHz, using an inductor L_1 for resistor R_1 in Fig. 10.4a. L_1C_1 is *not* tuned to resonance.

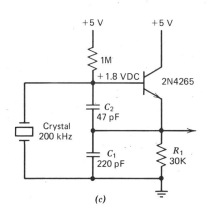

Figure 10.4(c). Colpitts-transistor at 200 kHz. Crystal shunt resistance must be $\geq$ 470K Ω for no loading effects and $\geq$ 220K Ω for oscillation to occur.

118

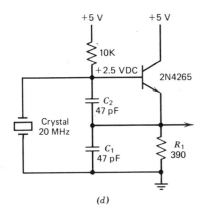

(d)

Figure 10.4(d). Colpitts-transitor at 20 MHz. Crystal shunt resistance must be $\geq$ 22K Ω for no loading effects and $\geq$ 2.2K Ω for oscillation to occur.

is about the lowest frequency at which a transistor-Colpitts circuit will work because of crystal loading effects. Below 1 MHz, oscillation amplitude is quite low because of crystal loading by the transistor. At frequencies below 1 MHz, a FET is a better choice than a transistor for the Colpitts circuit. A transistor-Colpitts circuit for operation at 20 MHz is shown in Fig. 10.4d.

10.5. LOW CAPACITANCE LOAD

A schematic of this circuit is shown in Fig. 10.5a. The circuit shows good performance; its short-term stability is a good 0.1 ppm. One criticism is that the crystal driving waveform could be more symmetrical than it actually is. As can be seen from the waveforms, the FET input signal is so large that it effectively turns the FET on and off like a half-wave rectifier. Increasing C_2 would help square up the crystal driving waveform. When the FET amplifier input saturates on the positive signal peaks, the only effect on the crystal is that capacitive divider impedance changes from 9.5 to 12 pF. Amplifier gain from point A to point C in Fig. 10.5a is only 0.8X, and additional gain is provided by partial resonance of C_1 and C_2 in series with the crystal's internal inductance.

Measuring the crystal current by means of the voltage drop across the series capacitor C_2 introduces a 90° phase lag. The RC networks R_3C_3 and R_4C_4 each introduce an additional 45° phase lag, and the transistor inverts the signal, providing a total phase shift of 360° around the amplifier loop.

Due to the low capacitance load effectively in series with the crystal, the oscillation frequency is about 300 ppm higher than it would be with a low impedance load. This is as expected and what normally occurs in an

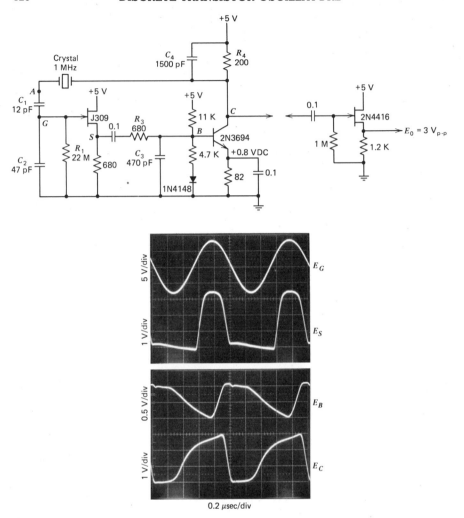

Figure 10.5(a). Low-capacitance load circuit at 1 MHz.

oscillator circuit when a small frequency-trimming capacitance is put in series with the crystal.

Are the low capacitance divider and the high resistance of the FET amplifier input effective in reducing resistive load losses? The answer is yes. Figures 10.5b–d show the equivalent crystal load circuit. Converting the parallel RC network of C_2 (47 pF) and R_1 (22 MΩ) to its series equivalent gives 47 pF and 0.6 Ω. The 0.6 Ω is negligible. The largest resistive loss comes from the driving source resistance R_4. Since R_4C_4 is shorted to ground by the transistor every half cycle, the effective R_4C_4 impedance values are halved, or 3000 pF and 100 Ω average over the complete waveform cycle, as shown in Fig. 10.5b. The final equivalent

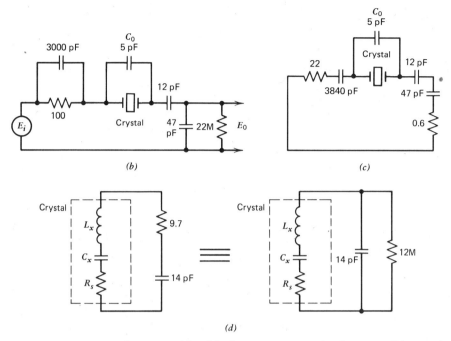

Figure 10.5. Equivalent crystal load for low-capacitance load circuit: (*b*) crystal load circuit, (*c*) intermediate, and (*d*) equivalent load circuits.

load on the crystal is 9.7 Ω in series with 14 pF, as shown in Fig. 10.5*d*. The low 9.7-Ω series resistance is the major reason for the circuit's good short-term frequency stability of 0.1 ppm.

Converting the averaged parallel R_4C_4 network in Fig. 10.5*b* to its series equivalent gives 3840 pF and 22 Ω, as shown in Fig. 10.5*c*. This series 22-Ω equivalent resistance is only 9% of the crystal's internal series resistance R_s of 240 Ω. Making the source resistance smaller would not improve the circuit Q very much. Note that in addition to providing a needed 45° phase lag, C_4 is also effective in reducing the crystal's driving source resistance $0.5R_4$ from 100 to 22 Ω.

10.6. HIGH RESISTANCE LOAD

The schematic of this circuit is illustrated in Fig. 10.6*a*. The circuit shows fair performance and has reasonably good short-term frequency stability of 0.2 ppm. One criticism is that the crystal's driving waveform could be more symmetrical than it actually is. As can be seen from the waveforms in Fig. 10.6*a*, the FET's input signal is so large that it effectively turns the FET on and off like a half-wave rectifier. Increasing the

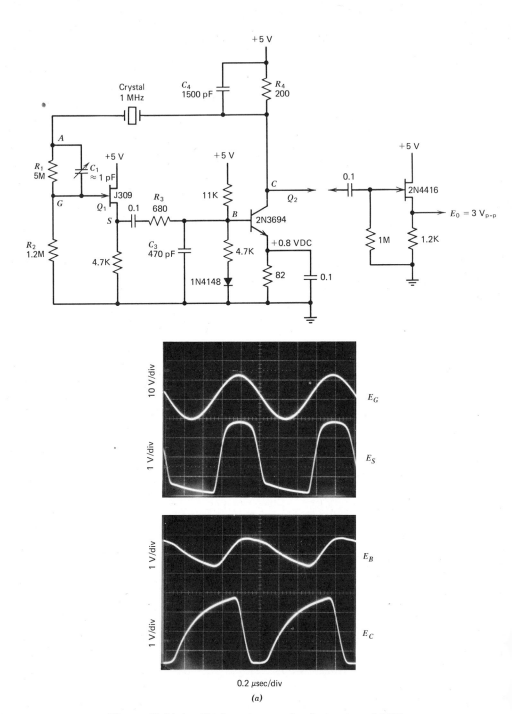

Figure 10.6(a). High-resistance load circuit at 1 MHz.

voltage divider ratio (i.e., reducing R_2) at the FET input would help square up the waveform.

When the FET amplifier saturates on the positive signal peaks, the only effect on the crystal is that its capacitive load increases from 5.8 to 6.0 pF. Amplifier gain from point A to point C in Fig. 10.6a is only 0.8X, and additional gain for circuit oscillation is provided by partial resonance of part of the crystal's inductance with the series combination of C_1 and the FET's input capacitance of 4 pF.

What sort of load does the crystal see in this circuit? It sees a capacitive load, consisting mostly of the crystal's own terminal capacitance C_0 (about 5 pF). The FET has an input capacitance of 4 pF directly across R_2. To frequency compensate the voltage divider, about 1 pF is added across R_1. The impedance of these two capacitors at 1 MHz is much lower than the resistance values of R_1 and R_2, which means that the voltage divider is effectively capacitive rather than resistive.

Due to the small 5-pF capacitance of the load effectively in series with the crystal, the oscillation frequency is 670 ppm higher than it would be with a low impedance load; this is as expected. Figures 10.6b–d show

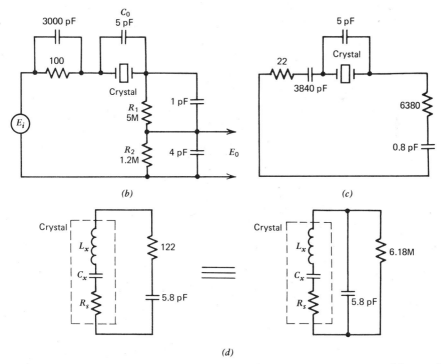

Figure 10.6. Equivalent crystal load for high-resistance load circuit: (b) crystal load circuit, (c) intermediate, and (d) equivalent load circuits.

the equivalent circuit. As can be seen from Fig. 10.6d, the equivalent series RC load on the crystal is 122 Ω and 5.8 pF. The crystal's internal series resistance R_s is 240 Ω, so that the external 122 Ω adds about 50% more, a reasonably small amount in practice. Figure 10.6c shows that most of the external 122-Ω load resistance comes from the high-resistance voltage divider, which means voltage-divider resistances could have been higher. Higher values of 10 and 2.4 MΩ, respectively, for R_1 and R_2 would have reduced equivalent series load resistance in half, to 61 Ω, a reasonable improvement in circuit Q.

This circuit provides a good example of what happens when we put a high resistance load on the crystal. The resonant frequency rises significantly, and a 90° phase lag occurs that must be compensated for in the amplifier. The 90° phase lag is due to measuring the crystal current by means of the voltage across a capacitor (effectively) rather than across a resistor. Two RC networks R_3C_3 and R_4C_4 are added internally in the amplifier, with each providing 45° of phase lag. Transistor Q_2 inverts the signal, giving a total of 360° phase shift around the loop.

10.7. COMMON BASE-TRANSISTOR

The schematic of this circuit at 1 MHz is shown in Fig. 10.7a. The circuit works very nicely. The crystal's internal series resistance R_s is 240 Ω, driving impedance is 10 Ω, and load impedance is 40 Ω. The in-circuit Q is degraded from the crystal's internal Q by $(240 + 40 + 10)/240 = 1.2$, which is quite reasonable. Waveforms at points A and B in Fig. 10.7a show that both transistors stay on over the complete waveform cycle, maintaining their low source and load resistances. The diode amplitude clamp works very well in this circuit. This common base oscillator circuit can be used up to 20 MHz by decreasing the emitter input resistance of Q_1 at point A in order to provide the lower load resistance needed by the crystal at higher frequencies. Increasing the emitter current of Q_1 will decrease its emitter input resistance.

Figure 10.7b shows a low frequency variation of the common base amplifier circuit operating at 4 kHz. This circuit also works very well. Here, the crystal is moved to a higher impedance point between collector and base, and the two emitters are tied together. The 4-kHz crystal's internal series resistance is 45K Ω, the source resistance is half of R_1 or 5K Ω, and the load resistance is 11K Ω. This gives an in-circuit reduction of the crystal's internal Q of $(45K + 5K + 11K)/45K = 1.4$, a reasonable value. The capacitor C_1 is added to the circuit to reduce noise at the sine

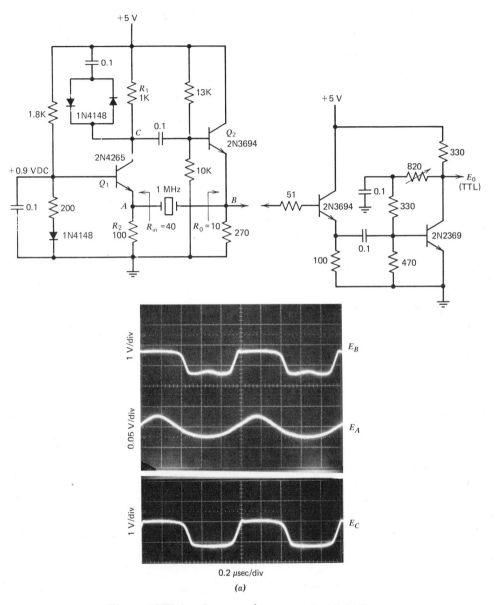

Figure 10.7(a). Common base circuit at 1 MHz.

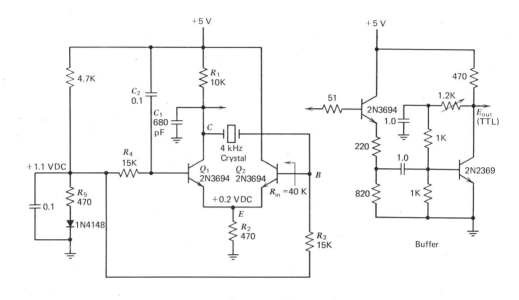

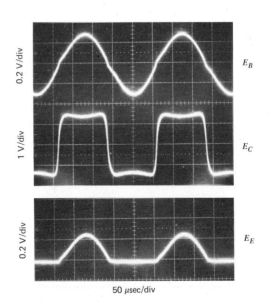

0.2 V/div

1 V/div

0.2 V/div

E_B

E_C

E_E

50 μsec/div

Figure 10.7(b). Common base circuit at 4 kHz ($R_s = 45K\,\Omega$). For operation at 50 kHz ($R_s = 20K\,\Omega$), use $R_1 = R_3 = R_4 = 4.7K\,\Omega$ and $C_1 = 220$ pF.

wave cross-over switching points in order to avoid multiple on-off switchings of Q_2 due to noise. This circuit also works well at 50 kHz by using circuit values given in the caption to Fig. 10.7b.

The emitter waveform at point E in Fig. 10.7b is rather interesting; it looks like the output of a half-wave rectifier. The half sine wave occurs when the base of Q_2 goes positive, pulling up the emitter voltage at point E. The waveform goes flat when the base of Q_2 goes negative and turns Q_2 off, which pulls Q_1 into a full-on state.

10.8. COMMON BASE-FET

The schematic of this circuit at 1 MHz is shown in Fig. 10.8; this circuit works very nicely. The 1-MHz crystal's internal series resistance is 240 Ω, source resistance is 10 Ω, and load resistance is 200 Ω. This gives an in-circuit Q reduction of $(240 + 200 + 10)/240 = 1.9$. A high transconductance FET like the J309 or U309 is required to get the FET's source input resistance down to 200 Ω. At lower frequencies, where a higher crystal load resistance is desired to avoid excessive gain loss, a FET of normal transconductance like the 2N4416 will provide a source input resistance of about 500 Ω. Waveform photographs show that both the FET and transistor stay in the linear region and maintain constant source and load resistances for the crystal over the complete waveform cycle. This is due to the use of the diode clamp for voltage limiting.

10.9. PIERCE

The schematic of this circuit for 1-MHz operation is shown in Fig. 10.9a; the circuit works very well. One criticism is that the crystal's driving waveform could be more symmetrical than it actually is. The short-term stability measures a very good 0.1 ppm.

Figures 10.9b and c show the equivalent series RC load seen by the crystal in Fig. 10.9a. The output resistance of the transistor stage is averaged at 500 Ω, halfway between the on- and off-state values of 0 and 1000 Ω, respectively. Figure 10.9c shows that the crystal's equivalent series load resistance is a low 25 Ω. This is only 10% of the crystal's internal series resistance of 240 Ω, so that in-circuit Q is only 10% less than the crystal's inherent Q. The low equivalent load resistance with respect to the crystal's internal series resistance R_s is the primary reason for the Pierce circuit's very good short-term frequency stability.

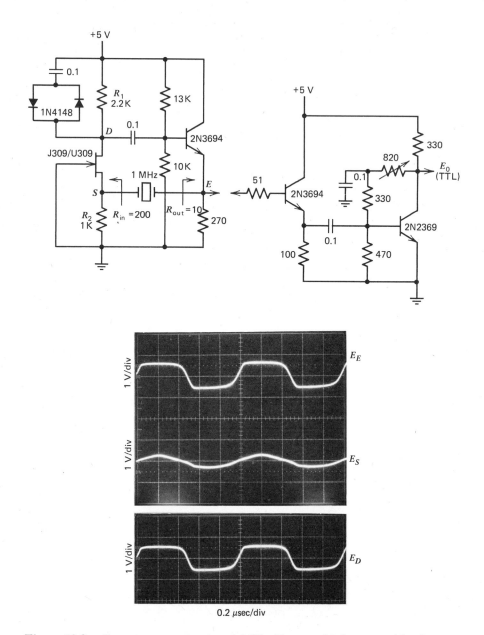

Figure 10.8. Common gate circuit at 1 MHz. To get a higher crystal load resistance (R_{in}) of 500 Ω at lower frequencies, substitute 2N4416 for U309, and use R_1 = 3.3K Ω, R_2 = 1.5K Ω.

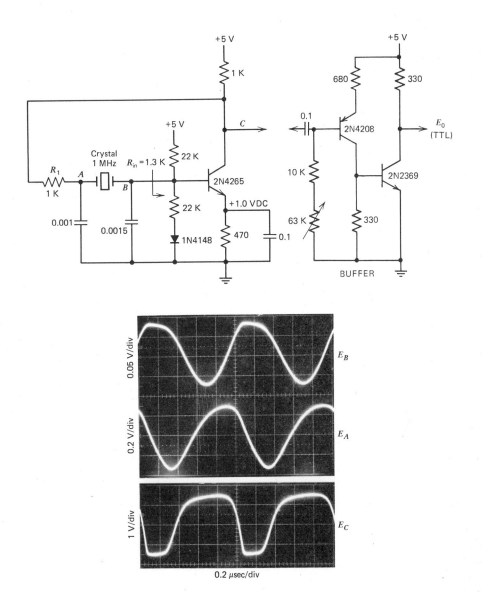

Figure 10.9(a). Pierce at 1 MHz.

129

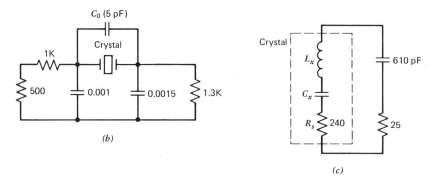

Figure 10.9. Equivalent crystal load for the 1-MHz Pierce circuit in Fig. 10.9a: (b) crystal load circuit and (c) equivalent circuit.

A schematic for a low frequency Pierce circuit at 4 kHz is shown in Fig. 10.9d. The main change here is the use of a FET source follower to avoid loading the crystal, which has a high internal resistance R_s of 45K Ω. This circuit works very well.

Figures 10.9e and f show the equivalent series RC load seen by the crystal in Fig. 10.9d. The output resistance of the transistor stage is averaged at 1000 Ω, halfway between the on- and off-state values of 0 and 2000 Ω, respectively. Figure 10.9f shows that the crystal's equivalent series load resistance is only 1040 Ω, about 2% of the crystal's internal series resistance of 45K Ω. This means that in-circuit Q is down only 2% from the crystal's inherent internal Q.

A schematic for a high-frequency Pierce circuit at 20 MHz is shown in Fig. 10.9g; this circuit works very well also. In this circuit, two emitter

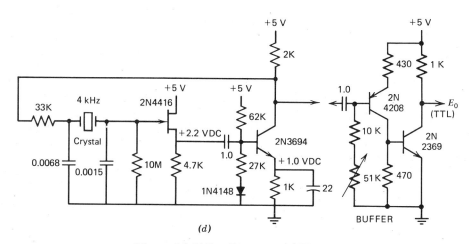

Figure 10.9(d). Pierce at 4 kHz.

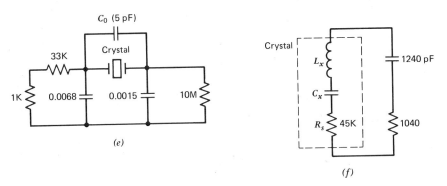

Figure 10.9. Equivalent crystal load for the 4-kHz Pierce circuit in Fig. 10.9*d*:
(*e*) crystal load circuit and (*f*) equivalent load circuit.

followers have been added at the amplifier output to permit driving the
low impedance crystal circuit. The 2N2369 requires a heat sink. R_1 is
selected on the basis that 30 Ω is the smallest resistance that the 2N2369
can drive without distortion. One change that might be made in this circuit would be to replace the 2N2369, which draws a lot of current, with a
step-down transformer. This would raise the low impedance of the crystal circuit to something the 2N5179 emitter follower could drive directly.

Figures 10.9*h* and *i* show the equivalent series RC load seen by the
crystal at 20 MHz in Fig. 10.9*g*. The equivalent series load resistance is
1.8 Ω, which is only 12% of the crystal's internal series resistance of 15 Ω.

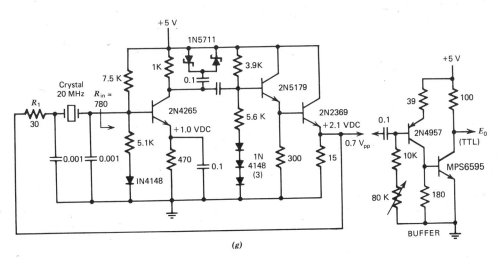

Figure 10.9(*g*). Pierce at 20 MHz.

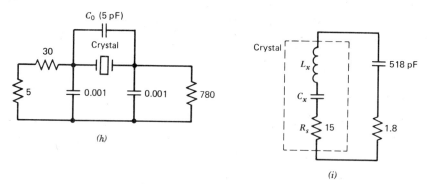

Figure 10.9. Equivalent crystal load for the 20-MHz Pierce circuit in Fig. 10.9g: (*h*) crystal load circuit and (*i*) equivalent load circuit.

The in-circuit Q of this 20-MHz Pierce circuit is down only 12% from the crystal's inherent internal Q.

10.10.   PIERCE AT EXACT SERIES RESONANCE

The schematic of this circuit at 1 MHz is shown in Fig. 10.10*a*. Three 60° RC lag networks are used to generate the 180° phase shift needed to operate the crystal at exact series resonance. It is convenient to increase R_1 to 100 Ω to give the emitter follower Q_2 an easier load to drive. This raises the R_1C_1 phase shift from 60 to 70°. To compensate for this, the R_2C_3 phase shift is decreased from 60 to 50°. A heat sink is required for the emitter follower Q_2. C_2 is selected so that its phase shift with the crystal's internal series resistance R_s is 60°. This circuit works very well and shows a 0.1-ppm frequency stability.

Figure 10.10*b* and *c* show the equivalent series RC load seen by the crystal in Fig. 10.10*a*. The equivalent series load resistance is only 18 Ω or 8% of the crystal's internal series resistance of 240 Ω. This means that in-circuit Q is only 8% lower than the crystal's inherent internal Q.

Do we gain anything by operating the crystal at exact series resonance instead of just near it? Yes and no. One advantage of the exact series-resonant circuit is its lower loop gain losses, which permit using a lower-gain transistor. There may or may not be a difference in the crystal's long-term drift stability by operating it at exact series resonance; short-term stability measures about the same. The exact resonance circuit is more complex, however, since it uses two transistors instead of one and three RC networks instead of two. With a little more design work, it might be possible to eliminate the second transistor.

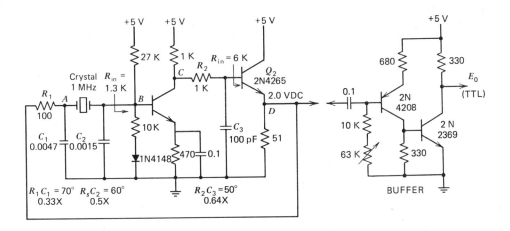

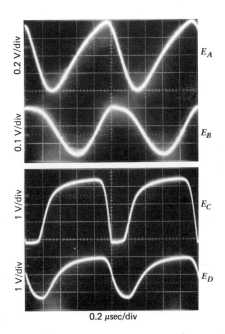

Fig. 10.10(a). Pierce at exact series resonance, at 1 MHz.

133

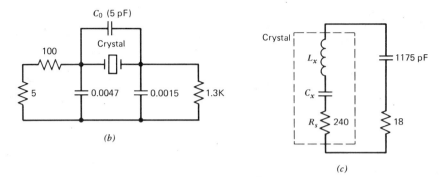

Figure 10.10. Equivalent crystal load for the 1-MHz Pierce circuit in Fig. 10.10a: (*b*) crystal load circuit and (*c*) equivalent load circuit.

10.11. PIERCE WITHOUT SERIES RESISTOR

The standard Pierce circuit in Fig. 10.9a is occasionally seen without the series resistor R_1. This reduces gain losses in the circuit and allows operation with a medium gain transistor instead of the high-gain transistor required by the standard Pierce circuit. The main drawback is that the crystal operates at a higher voltage level. If the circuit is used above 4 MHz, the crystal's power dissipation should be checked in order to be sure it is within the dissipation limit.

Figure 10.11a shows a Pierce oscillator circuit without the series resistor R_1. This circuit is identical to the one in Fig. 10.9a except that R_1 is eliminated. Waveform photographs in each figure allow a direct comparison of the difference. When R_1 is eliminated, its function in the R_1C_1 phase-shift network in Fig. 10.11a is replaced by the parallel resistance of R_2 and the output resistance of Q_1's collector.

Figures 10.11b and c show the equivalent series RC load seen by the crystal. The equivalent series load resistance is 54 Ω or 23% of the crystal's internal series resistance of 240 Ω. This gives an in-circuit Q only 23% lower than the crystal's inherent internal Q.

10.12. EMITTER COUPLED

The schematic of this circuit at 1 MHz is shown in Fig. 10.12. This circuit works fairly well and has a very good short-term frequency stability of 0.1 ppm. The crystal also has a good waveform across it.

The loop gain with the crystal removed from the circuit is set at slightly less than 1X (about 0.8X). The ratio of collector to emitter resis-

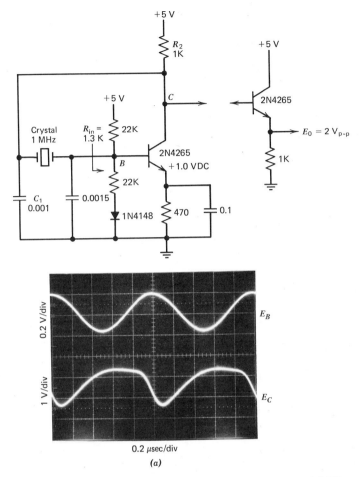

Figure 10.11(*a*). Pierce without a series resistor, at 1 MHz.

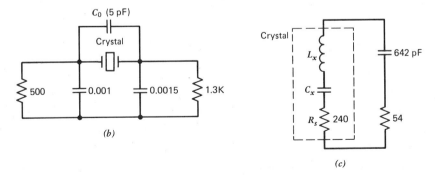

Figure 10.11.   Pierce without a series resistor, at 1 MHz: (*a*) schematic, (*b*) crystal load circuit, and (*c*) equivalent crystal load circuit.

135

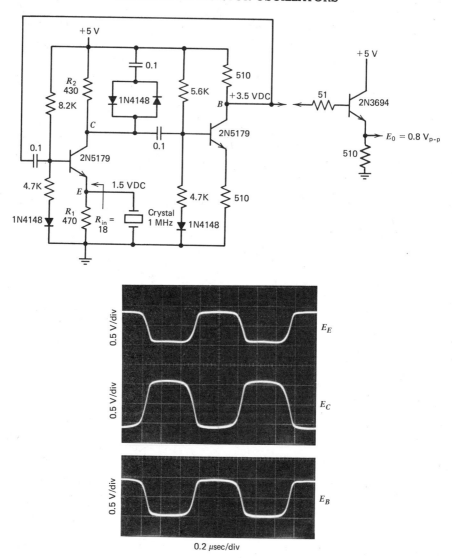

Figure 10.12. Emitter coupled circuit at 1 MHz.

tances in the first stage is 0.9, and loading effects from the second stage cut the actual first stage gain another 10% to 0.8X. The second stage has a gain of 1X and inverts the signal to provide positive feedback. The 1-MHz crystal has an internal series resistance R_s of 240 Ω. The emitter resistor shunting the crystal is set at about twice the crystal's internal resistance or 470 Ω. Because the loop gain is just short of 1X over a wide frequency range, circuit waveforms are sensitive to stray capacitance effects.

To obtain a good waveform across the crystal, a diode amplitude clamp must be used across the collector resistor R_2 in the first stage. The resulting low signal amplitude prevents the emitter current from going to zero and keeps the crystal's load resistance at a desirably low value. The crystal's low load resistance is the transistor emitter's input resistance R_{in}, which is 18 Ω in Fig. 10.12. This low load resistance on the crystal is the primary reason for the circuit's very good short-term stability. If the emitter current were to go to zero, the load on the crystal would increase from the 18-Ω input resistance of the emitter to the 470 Ω of the emitter resistor R_1. The diode clamp also keeps the first stage transistor from saturating, which would increase the crystal's load resistance if it occurred.

10.13. MODIFIED MEACHAM

A schematic of the modified Meacham half-bridge circuit at 1 MHz is shown in Fig. 10.13 a. It is a complex circuit with good performance and operates at series resonance. Its short-term frequency stability is particularly good, being as good as or better than 0.1 ppm, the limit of available measuring equipment. It was not possible to tell whether the 0.1-ppm frequency variation observed was in the circuit or the frequency-measuring equipment. Figure 10.13b shows voltage waveforms at various points in the circuit. The somewhat peculiar waveform shown at the bridge output (E_A in Fig. 10.13b) is normal and results from the bridge subtracting a square wave with sloping sides (through bridge arm R_2) from a sine wave (through the crystal arm).

The circuit uses a two-stage amplifier, with a gain of 28X from point A to point B in Fig. 10.13a. The split-load phase inverter Q_1 provides a 2 to 1 half-bridge, with the emitter resistor twice as large as the collector resistor. C_2 is twice as large as the crystal's shunt terminal capacitance C_0 of 3.5 pF in order to balance the half-bridge capacitively. C_2 is more important than it looks, since the signal path through C_0 provides positive feedback, which tends to make the amplifier oscillate, while the signal path through C_2 provides negative feedback and stabilizes the amplifier. C_3 improves the high-frequency phase response of Q_1's collector, so that its high-frequency response is flat out to 80 MHz. The value of C_3 is determined experimentally, and its use helps considerably in preventing high-frequency parasitic oscillation.

For maximum frequency stability and maximum in-circuit Q, it is desirable to use the smallest possible value of R_2. With a 2 to 1 half-bridge,

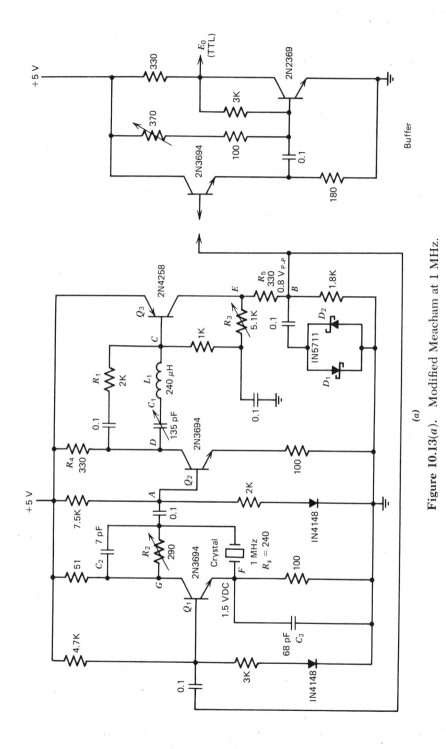

Figure 10.13(a). Modified Meacham at 1 MHz.

138

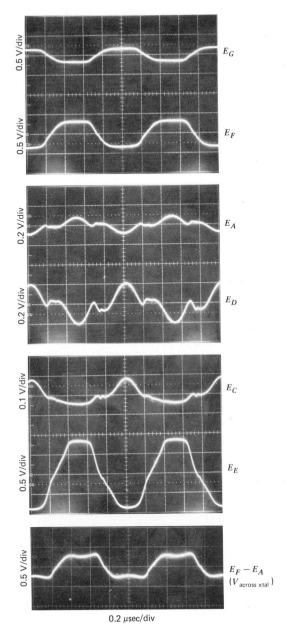

Figure 10.13(b). Waveforms for modified Meacham circuit in Fig. 10.13a.

139

the minimum theoretical value of R_2 for the circuit to oscillate is equal to one-half the crystal's internal series resistance R_s. The 1-MHz crystal used has an internal resistance of 240 Ω, so the minimum value for R_2 is 120 Ω. The circuit will not oscillate except parasitically when R_2 is less than its theoretical minimum value of 120 Ω, so this condition makes a good test for parasitics. The circuit in Fig. 10.13a does not oscillate when R_2 is less than 120 Ω, indicating a stable amplifier design. In practice, R_2 has to be slightly larger than 0.5 R_s for the circuit to oscillate, the exact amount depending on amplifier gain. In Fig. 10.13a, a practical value for R_2 is 290 Ω, a small amount more than the bare minimum needed for oscillation, to ensure that the circuit will oscillate under all conditions. This gives a ratio of practical to theoretical minimum values of 290/120 or 2.4. This ratio of 2.4 for R_2 provides a measure of the crystal's in-circuit Q, with the unattainable ratio of one corresponding to infinite Q.

The amplifier stage Q_2 is designed to present a reasonably high load resistance to the half-bridge and drive the relatively low input resistance of Q_3's base-emitter junction. The second amplifier stage drives the diode clamp, D_1-D_2. Resistor R_5 provides a source resistance for the diode clamp to work against. The feedback resistor R_3 adjusts the on/off ratio of the clamped square wave to 1.0.

The circuit uses one resonant LC circuit, tuned to the frequency of oscillation, to reduce the circuit's frequency response away from resonance. Tuning the LC circuit has a considerable effect on the circuit's oscillation frequency, so both L_1 and C_1 must be stable components. L_1 must be an air core inductor, and C_1 must be adjustable to 1% for close tuning. Note that L_1C_1 is shunted by a resistance R_1, which corrects the 90° phase shift of L_1C_1 back to 0° at frequencies far away from resonance. This helps stabilize the circuit and prevent parasitic oscillation.

Figure 10.13c shows a modified Meacham circuit for 10-MHz operation. This circuit performs well; its short-term stability is 0.1 ppm, at the limit of available measuring equipment. The circuit uses a three-stage amplifier that is different in several respects from the one used at 1 MHz. The differences are primarily due to the crystal's much lower internal series resistance R_s at 10 MHz. First, the split-load phase inverter Q_1 has much lower emitter and collector resistors, so that Q_1 can drive the low 5-Ω resistance of the 10-MHz crystal. Second, an emitter follower Q_4 has been added to drive the low input resistance of the phase inverter Q_1. And third, the L_1C_1 tank circuit for rolling off frequencies away from resonance has been moved to the emitter of Q_2, where it increases the gain of Q_2 at frequencies near resonance. The base input resistance of Q_2 is low with this arrangement, but it is still relatively high with respect

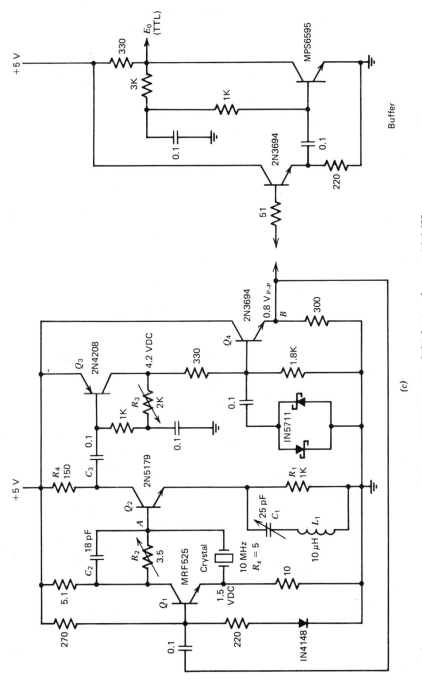

Figure 10.13(c). Modified Meacham at 10 MHz.

141

to the very low resistance of R_2 and the crystal's internal resistance R_s, so it does not load the half-bridge significantly. L_1C_1 is deliberately shunted with R_1 in order to reduce the 90° phase shift of L_1C_1 at frequencies far away from resonance back to 0°.

The circuit uses a 2 to 1 half-bridge, so C_2 in Fig. 10.13b is set equal to twice the crystal's shunt terminal capacitance C_0 of 8.5 pF. The theoretical minimum value of R_2 in this circuit is 0.5 R_s or 2.5 Ω. The practical value of R_2, set at just slightly more than the minimum value for oscillation, is 3.5 Ω. This gives a practical to theoretical minimum ratio of 3.5/2.5 or 1.4 for R_2.

The voltage gain of the amplifier from point A to point B in Fig. 10.13c is 50X. The amplifier is stable and does not oscillate when R_2 is set below its minimum theoretical value for oscillation of 2.5 Ω. A heat sink is required on transistor Q_1.

Figure 10.13d shows a modified Meacham circuit for 100-kHz operation. This circuit works well and has a short-term frequency stability of 0.1 ppm, at the limit of available measuring equipment. The circuit uses a three-stage amplifier and differs in several respects from the one used at 1 MHz, primarily because of the crystal's higher internal resistance at 100 kHz. An emitter follower Q_4 is used at the bridge output to prevent the amplifier from loading the bridge. The tuned circuit L_1C_1 is moved to the emitter of Q_2 and increases the gain of Q_2 at resonance. The low input resistance of Q_2 at resonance is easily driven by the emitter follower Q_4. L_1C_1 is shunted with a resistor R_1 to reduce the 90° phase shift of L_1C_1 at frequencies far away from resonance back to 0°.

Q_3 is a combination amplifier and diode amplitude clamp and gives a fixed on/off ratio to its square wave output that is very close to 1.0. The on/off ratio is independent of power supply or bias changes. R_3 trims the waveform flatness at the top and bottom of the square wave out of Q_3.

Because of the 2 to 1 bridge ratio set by Q_1's emitter-to-collector-resistance ratio, C_2 is set equal to twice the crystal's terminal shunt capacitance C_0 of 8 pF. The theoretical minimum value of R_2 is one-half of the crystal's internal series resistance R_s or 200 Ω, again because of the bridge's 2 to 1 ratio. The practical minimum value of R_2, set at slightly more than the minimum required for oscillation, is 420 Ω. This gives a practical-to-theoretical minimum ratio of 420/200 or 2.1 for R_2 in Fig. 10.13d. The amplifier is stable and does not oscillate when R_2 is set below the minimum theoretical value for oscillation. The amplifier has a gain of 100X from point A to point B in Fig. 10.13d.

Although the modified Meacham circuits described here work well, the amplifiers used in them can probably be simplified and improved.

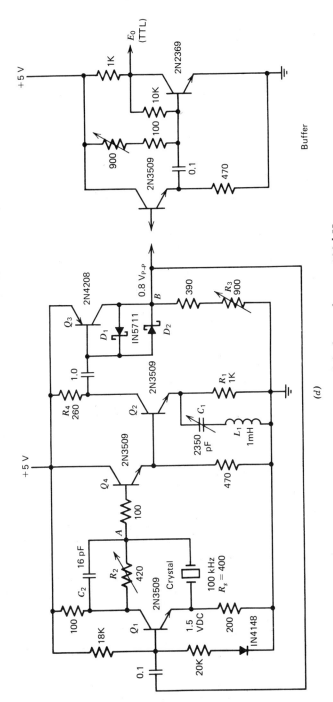

Figure 10.13(d). Modified Meacham at 100 kHz.

143

One approach would be to combine the best parts of the three amplifiers into one. Such an amplifier would include: (1) a shunt capacitor C_3 across the Q_1 phase splitter's emitter resistor to correct the high-frequency phase response at the phase splitter's collector, as in Fig. 10.13a; (2) a series L_1C_1 network across Q_2's emitter resistor R_1 in order to amplify only the desired oscillation frequency, as in Figs. 10.13c and d; and (3) putting the diode amplitude clamp between Q_3's base and collector, as in Fig. 10.13d. Another approach would be to put the L_1C_1 filter after the diode amplitude clamp in the amplifier, so that the crystal is driven with a sine wave instead of a square wave.

C. HARMONIC CIRCUITS

10.14. COLPITTS (20 MHz)

The schematic of this harmonic oscillator is shown in Fig. 10.14. This 20-MHz harmonic circuit is the same as the 20-MHz fundamental circuit shown in Fig. 10.4d except that the 390-Ω emitter resistor R_1 is replaced with a 3.2-μH inductor whose impedance (410 Ω at 20 MHz) is approximately equal to the resistance of R_1. The bias resistor R_2 is also increased to 470K Ω, to accommodate the DC voltage shift when R_1 is removed. The voltage swing at both the base and emitter terminals is a large 10 Vp-p (+5 to −5 VDC).

Circuit performance is rated fair. The strong point of this circuit is its low parts count. Its frequency is somewhat sensitive to power supply changes, however. In an effort to reduce this sensitivity, the base biasing

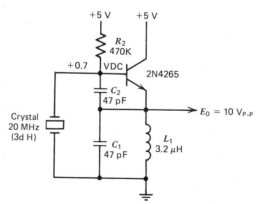

Figure 10.14. Colpitts harmonic circuit at 20 MHz. Crystal shunt resistance must be $\geq$ 22K Ω for no loading effects and $\geq$ 2.2K Ω for oscillation to occur.

resistor R_2 was replaced with a FET constant current source, but this did not help.

10.15. BUTLER COMMON BASE (20 MHz, C-TAP)

The schematic of this VHF harmonic oscillator is shown in Fig. 10.15. The crystal operates at its third harmonic. Bad parasitics seem to be inherent in the Butler common base circuit, and it requires considerable experimental effort to come up with a satisfactory parts layout. Even then, several parasitics usually remain. We end up satisfied if the tank circuit will tune properly without spurious oscillations just at the frequency desired. R_2 and R_3 help damp down parasitic effects considerably and also help isolate external load-capacitance effects from the tuned circuit.

Diode D_1 helps stabilize the collector current against a varying power supply voltage, but it does not help enough. The collector current still varies too much. The circuit works better (less lead inductance?) if C_2 is tied directly to the grounded end of the emitter resistor R_1, as shown in Fig. 10.15, rather than to +5 VDC, as shown in Fig. 5.28. The emitter waveform shows that the transistor does not cut off and, thus, provides a reasonably constant low resistance load to the crystal over the complete waveform. The diode clamp ensures that the transistor does not saturate and keeps the oscillation amplitude within the transistor's linear region. The crystal's load resistance is about 10 Ω, and its internal series resistance is about 40 Ω. This gives a voltage-divider gain loss of 10/(10 + 40) or 0.20. The crystal's capacitive source impedance is between one and two times the impedance of C_2 (35 Ω), depending on the value of C_1. The circuit's frequency sensitivity to temperature depends on the collector current and varies two to one over the operating range of collector current.

To oscillate properly, the collector current must be set at a specific value. Below this value, the circuit will not oscillate; above this value, oscillation ceases. If the emitter current is increased even further, the circuit will start oscillating again at some other frequency, either at a harmonic or at some other spurious frequency.

Waveforms in Fig. 10.15 show a 40° phase lag from point E to point C and a 60° phase lead from point C to point A, with the crystal and its resistive load providing a 20° phase lag from point A to point E. Tuning C_1 will change the crystal's phase shift from lag to zero (series resonance) to lead, with the other two phase angles changing accordingly, so that they always add up to zero.

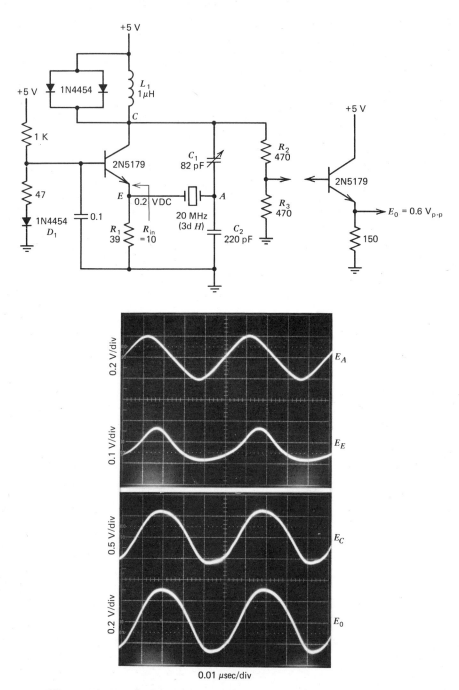

Figure 10.15. Butler common base at 20 MHz, capacitive tap.

146

This circuit works satisfactorily once we get past the parasitics. But its basic design defect of oscillating only over a narrow range of collector current, and its bad parasitics, make it only a poor to fair circuit.

10.16. BUTLER COMMON BASE (20 MHz, L-TAP)

The schematic of this VHF harmonic oscillator is shown in Fig. 10.16. The purpose of this circuit is to find out if an inductive tap offers anything useful over a capacitive tap. The circuit is the same as the one in Fig. 10.15 except that the crystal is tapped down on the inductor in the LC tank instead of on the capacitor. The biggest advantage of the L-tapped circuit is that it has no parasitics (assuming a reasonable parts layout), which makes it much easier to debug and tune. The biggest disadvantage is a lower oscillation frequency. The inductive tap introduces a phase lag in the circuit in comparison with a capacitive tap, which introduces a phase lead. The crystal must provide a large phase lead to compensate for the two phase lags of the LC tank circuit and the inductive tap (see Chapter 7). To provide the phase lead, the crystal must operate below series resonance, which is what gives the circuit its lower oscillation frequency. The phase lag from E to C in Fig. 10.16 is 50°. From C to A, the phase lag is 22°, and the crystal and its emitter load provide a 72° phase lead from A to E.

The frequency-temperature sensitivity varies 2 to 1 with the emitter current in both the L-tap and C-tap circuits. A minor disadvantage of the L-tap circuit is that it is harder to check. Putting the capacitive load of a scope probe (about 7 pF) at the inductive tap point A in Fig. 10.16 disturbs the circuit and adds unwanted oscillatory ripples to the waveform.

The circuit's overall performance is about the same with an inductive tap as with a capacitive tap. Either way, the circuit is rated only as a poor to fair VHF harmonic oscillator.

10.17. BUTLER COMMON BASE (50 MHz)

The schematic of this VHF harmonic oscillator, shown in Fig. 10.17, exhibits parasitic effects typical of this circuit. The 50-MHz third-harmonic crystal used had a relatively low series resistance of 25 Ω. The crystal's load impedance is 8 Ω. The crystal's capacitive source impedance is one to two times the impedance of C_2 (70 Ω), depending on the setting of C_1. The diode amplitude clamp across L_1 is very effective in keeping the

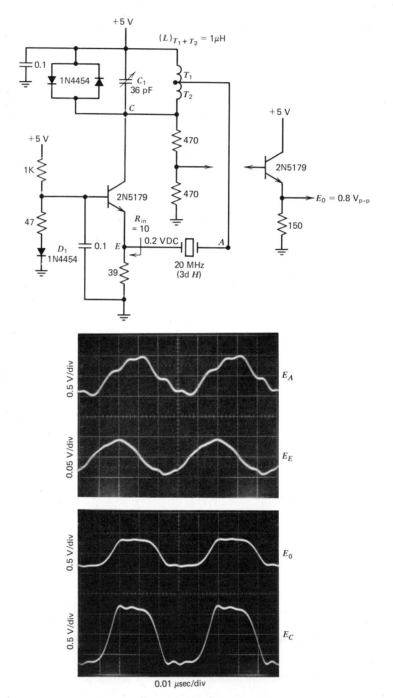

Figure 10.16. Butler common base at 20 MHz, inductive tap. $T_1 = 7$ turns, $T_2 = 19$ turns.

148

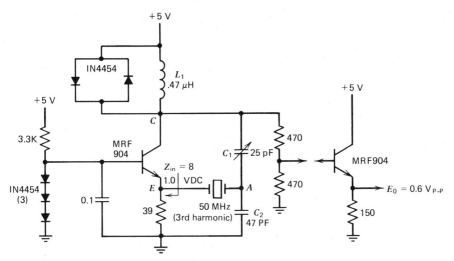

Figure 10.17. Butler common base at 50 MHz.

emitter drive voltage low, so that the transistor will stay in its linear region. The emitter then provides a low and constant load resistance to the crystal over the complete waveform cycle.

Circuit performance is only fair to poor due to its design defect of oscillating over only a narrow range of collector current and its bad parasitic effects.

10.18. BUTLER COMMON BASE (100 MHz, C-TAP)

The schematic of this VHF harmonic oscillator is shown in Fig. 10.18. The crystal operates at the fifth harmonic. Diodes D_1–D_3 provide a stabilized bias voltage source for the transistor. Diodes D_4 and D_5 limit oscillation amplitude and keep the transistor from saturating or shutting off at any part of the waveform cycle. The crystal's internal series resistance R_s is 70 Ω, and its load impedance is 8 Ω. The crystal's capacitive source impedance is one to two times the impedance of C_2 (100 Ω), depending on the value of C_1. The circuit can be set to exact series resonance by tuning C_1 so that the voltages at points A and E in Fig. 10.18 are in phase with each other. This assumes that the emitter's input impedance at E is a pure resistance and not reactive.

An adjustable inductor L_2 is placed across the crystal to tune out the crystal's terminal capacitance C_0 of 5.7 pF. L_2 can be an iron-core inductor, but L_1 must be an air-core unit. The circuit will still oscillate if L_2 is

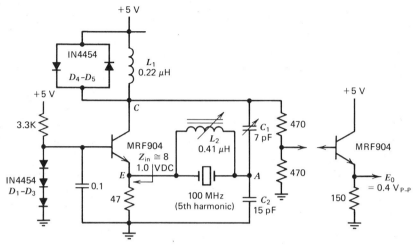

Figure 10.18. Butler common base at 100 MHz, capacitive tap.

not used, but frequency sensitivity to power supply variations is four times worse, and short-term frequency stability also degrades somewhat.

The performance of this circuit is only fair to poor due to the usual parasitics with this circuit and the circuit's design defect of oscillating over only a narrow range of collector current.

10.19. BUTLER COMMON BASE (100 MHz, L-TAP)

The schematic of this VHF harmonic oscillator is shown in Fig. 10.19. The purpose of this circuit is to try out Butler's idea [6] of canceling the crystal's terminal capacitance C_0 by adding an equal voltage of opposite phase through an equivalent capacitance C_2 to the crystal's output at the emitter. The opposite phase is obtained by extending L_1 a few turns beyond the normal +5 V power supply end of the coil.

The terminal-capacitance cancellation idea works poorly. The L_1 taps at T_1 and T_3 are low impedance. Circuit operation is quite sensitive to the length of the common lead wire from A and B in Fig. 11.19, which was about a half-inch long in the test circuit. Some sort of common mode effect in the common lead wire from A to B (probably lead inductance) seems to be present and requires an excessively large reverse-phase voltage $(T_3 > T_1)$ and a compensation capacitance C_2 that is 25% larger than the crystal's terminal capacitance C_0 to cancel out C_0. In addition, the oscillation frequency is unnecessarily sensitive to small changes in C_2 or C_1.

This circuit performs poorly. The idea of canceling out the crystal's

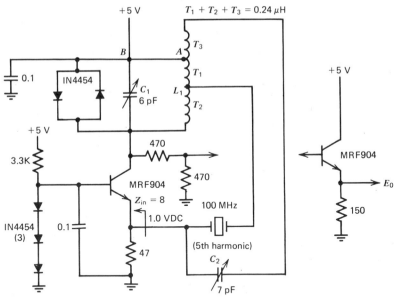

Figure 10.19. Butler common base at 100 MHz, inductive tap. $T_1 = 1.2$ turns, $T_2 = 2.6$ turns, $T_3 = 2.2$ turns.

terminal capacitance with a capacitance bridge circuit does not work well in practice.

10.20. BUTLER EMITTER FOLLOWER (20 MHz, C-TAP)

The schematic of this VHF harmonic oscillator is shown in Fig. 10.20. The crystal operates at the third harmonic and is tapped into the capacitive side of the LC tank. The circuit has no parasitic effects of any kind.

There are no 2.6 V Zener diodes available, so four signal diodes are cascaded in series for base biasing. The emitter's output resistance that drives the crystal is 25 Ω. The crystal's load impedance is mostly capacitive and is one to two times the impedance of C_2 (35 Ω), depending on the value of C_1. The crystal's internal series resistance R_s is 40 Ω.

This circuit works very well, and the absence of parasitics is a big help. By tuning C_i, the oscillation frequency can be set either at or slightly above (2 ppm) series resonance.

10.21. BUTLER EMITTER FOLLOWER (20 MHz, L-TAP)

The schematic of this VHF harmonic oscillator is shown in Fig. 10.21. The purpose of this circuit is to find out if an inductive tap offers anything more than a capacitive tap does. The crystal operates at the third

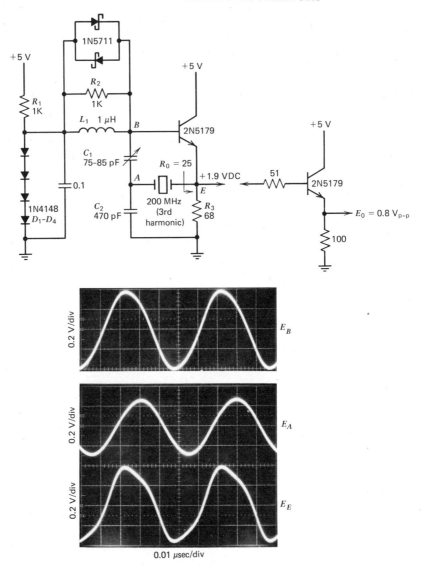

Figure 10.20. Butler emitter follower at 20 MHz, capacitive tap.

harmonic. The circuit is essentially the same as the one in Fig. 10.20
except that the crystal is tapped down on the inductor in the LC tank
instead of on the capacitor. The inductive tap introduces a phase lag in
the circuit, as compared with a capacitive tap, which introduces a phase
lead. The crystal must provide a phase lead to compensate for the phase
lag of the inductive tap, which means that the crystal must operate below
resonance. This gives the circuit a lower oscillation frequency compared
with the capacitive tap circuit.

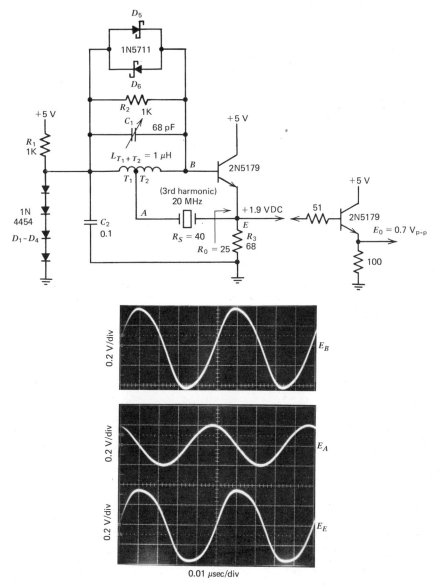

Figure 10.21. Butler emitter follower at 20 MHz, inductive tap. $T_1 = 4$ turns, $T_2 = 22$ turns.

There are no 2.6 V Zener diodes available, so four signal diodes are cascaded in series for base biasing. The emitter's output resistance driving the crystal is 25 Ω. The crystal's load impedance is mostly inductive and one to two times the 30-Ω inductive reactance of the tapped portion T_1 of the 1-μH inductor. The crystal's internal series resistance R_s is about 40 Ω. For good operation, the circuit requires a short coupled bypass capacitor C_2 from the grounded end of the inductor to the grounded end of the emitter resistor R_3, as shown in Fig. 10.21.

This circuit works very well, but it does not offer any advantages over the C-tap circuit. Neither the L-tap or C-tap circuits show any parasitic oscillation effects. However, the oscillation frequency with the L-tap is always slightly below series resonance (about 2 ppm). Tuning C_1 will vary the oscillation frequency from 3 to 1 ppm below series resonance.

Why this circuit will not oscillate at series resonance is not known. The analysis in Chapter 7 indicates that it should be possible. Removing the diode amplitude clamp D_5-D_6 will allow the circuit to oscillate at series resonance or even up to 2 ppm above it. But the emitter follower's source resistance that drives the crystal goes too high (the transistor shuts off over part of the oscillation cycle) for this to be a viable alternative.

10.22. BUTLER EMITTER FOLLOWER (50 MHz)

The schematic of this VHF harmonic oscillator is shown in Fig. 10.22. The crystal operates at the third harmonic and is tapped into the capacitive side of the LC tank. As is typical of this circuit, it has no parasitic oscillation effects. Since there are no 2.6 V Zeners available, four signal diodes in series are used for base biasing. The emitter's output impedance that drives the crystal is 29 Ω. The crystal's load impedance is

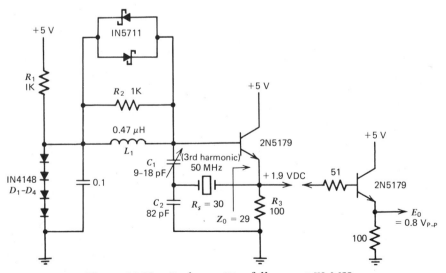

Figure 10.22. Butler emitter follower at 50 MHz.

mostly capacitive and one to two times the 40-Ω capacitive reactance of C_2, depending on the value of C_1. The crystal's internal series resistance R_s is 30 Ω. This is a good circuit and works very well without any problems.

10.23. BUTLER EMITTER FOLLOWER (100 MHz, C-TAP)

The schematic of this VHF harmonic oscillator is shown in Fig. 10.23. The crystal operates at the fifth harmonic and is tapped into the capacitive side of the LC tank. As is typical of this circuit, it has no parasitics. Since 2.6 V Zeners are not available, four signal diodes are cascaded in series for base biasing. The emitter's output impedance driving the crystal is 25 Ω. The crystal's load impedance is mostly capacitive and, depending on the value of C_1, is one to two times the 50 Ω impedance of C_2.

The crystal has a terminal capacitance C_0 of 4.2 pF and a capacitive reactance of 360 Ω at 100 MHz. This is tuned out of the circuit by a 0.41 μhenry inductor L_0 in parallel resonance across the crystal. The circuit will operate without the shunt inductor L_0, but the inductor provides a 4 to 10 times reduction in frequency sensitivity to power supply changes, which makes its use worthwhile. The oscillation amplitude at 100 MHz is low, so to give a larger oscillation amplitude fast-recovery signal di-

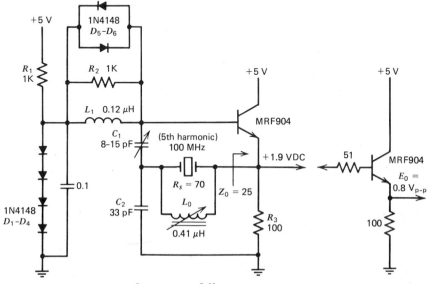

Figure 10.23. Butler emitter follower at 100 MHz, capacitive tap.

odes rather than Schottky diodes are used for the amplitude clamp D_5-D_6. This is a good circuit and works very well.

10.24. BUTLER EMITTER FOLLOWER (100 MHz, L-TAP)

The schematic of this VHF harmonic oscillator is shown in Fig. 10.24. The purpose of this circuit is to find out if Butler's out-of-phase subtraction scheme [6] for eliminating the crystal's terminal capacitance C_0 will work in the emitter follower circuit. The crystal operates at the fifth harmonic and is tapped into the inductive side of the LC tank. The crystal drive signal is fed through a capacitor C_2 to a reversed-phase tap on the inductor. If T_1 equals T_3 and C_2 equals the crystal's terminal capacitance C_0, then the two capacitances will cancel out one another.

To set up the bridge balance, the crystal and C_2 are disconnected from the emitter and driven in parallel by an external signal generator at a frequency somewhere near (but not at) the oscillation frequency. C_2 is then adjusted for minimum signal at the emitter. The external signal generator is disconnected, and the crystal and C_2 are reconnected to the emitter. The circuit then oscillates at or near the crystal's series-resonant frequency.

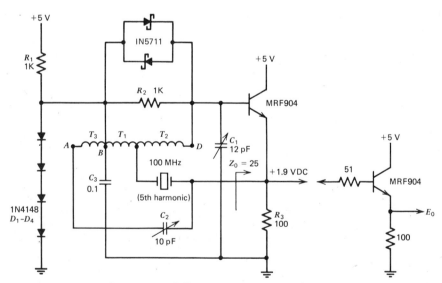

Figure 10.24. Butler emitter follower at 100 MHz, showing out-of-phase cancellation of the crystal's terminal capacitance C_0. $L_{AD} = 0.24\ \mu H$, 6 turns closewound on 0.28-in. diameter form. $T_1 = 1.2$ turns, $T_2 = 2.6$ turns, $T_3 = 2.2$ turns.

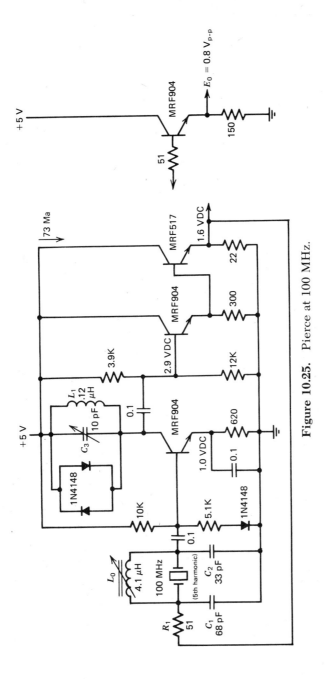

Figure 10.25. Pierce at 100 MHz.

157

This circuit does not work well at all; it performs poorly and tunes poorly. The out-of-phase cancellation idea works, but lopsidedly. At null balance, the capacitance C_2 is twice the crystal's terminal capacitance C_0, and T_3 has twice the turns of T_1. The circuit is very sensitive to the length (inductance?) of the ground lead in Fig. 10.24 from point B through the bypass capacitor C_3 to the grounded end of the emitter resistor R_3, as if there were a common mode effect present. Changing C_2 by 4 pF changes the oscillation frequency by 600 Hz, which is much too sensitive. And finally, the oscillation frequency of 99.996603 MHz is very low for a 100-MHz crystal.

10.25. PIERCE (100 MHz)

The schematic of this circuit is shown in Fig. 10.25. The crystal operates on the fifth harmonic. The first stage amplifier uses a tuned L_1C_3 tank as the collector load, with a diode amplitude limiter. The second and third stages are emitter followers to drop the high L_1C_3 tank impedance to about 5 Ω in order to drive the low impedance crystal circuit. L_1 has to have an air core in order to avoid the detuning effects of core saturation and its associated nonlinearities, but L_0 is less sensitive and can use an iron core. A heat sink is required on the MRF517.

The circuit works well and has relatively low sensitivity to power supply changes. The second emitter follower draws a large power supply current and is an obvious candidate for replacement by a step-down transformer in low power applications. The L_1C_3 tank tunes satisfactorily, but parasitics show up quickly when detuned. The circuit has a relatively high parts count.

CHAPTER ELEVEN

INTEGRATED CIRCUIT
OSCILLATORS

This chapter contains performance test data on individual IC oscillator circuits. It is divided into five parts, the first of which describes oscillator characteristics of various IC technologies and gives some general characteristics of various IC oscillator types. The second part covers series-resonant circuits, and the third covers Pierce circuits. Special oscillator ICs are discussed in the fourth part, and a VHF harmonic oscillator in the fifth.

A. CIRCUIT SELECTION

The basic principle in selecting IC oscillator circuits was to try as many types and kinds of ICs as possible, testing each one to find its strong and weak points. A total of 24 different IC oscillator circuits were built and tested, using ECL, TTL, CMOS, and LINEAR technologies. Eight were series-resonant circuits, six were Pierce circuits, and one was a VHF harmonic circuit. Nine more were special ICs, specifically designed to be used as crystal oscillators.

The search for a good IC that a quartz crystal would like was mainly for a circuit with linear input and binary (square wave) output. A gain of 2–60X was needed, the exact amount depending on the circuit used. Line receivers and voltage comparators have linear-input resistances and binary outputs, making them potentially good choices.

In general, TTL does not work too well in an oscillator circuit, because its input resistance is highly nonlinear at the switching point, and it exhibits bad parasitic oscillations if it does not switch rapidly between

159

its two binary output states. CMOS has good input characteristics, but it is pretty limited in its output-drive capability. In contrast, ECL is almost ideal for an oscillator circuit, with its high linear input resistance and low output resistance, combined with a good output-drive capability.

Some of the IC oscillator circuits tested were not TTL or CMOS compatible. Level shifters or buffers were added to these circuits to make them TTL compatible. After selection, each circuit was individually optimized by test for the best component values, bias, waveforms, and so forth. The ICs used have a strong effect on circuit performance, so considerable time was spent selecting the right one for each circuit. Most of the optimizing of the fundamental circuits was done at 1 MHz, and photographs were taken of waveforms at various points in the circuits. Just as with the discrete transistor circuits, waveform photographs were synchronized to a common point in time and vertically aligned together on the printed page. This permits vertical waveform comparisons at the same point in time between various parts of a circuit.

The same test philosophy was used in testing integrated circuits that was used in testing discrete transistor circuits. That test philosophy is described in Section 10A and will not be repeated here.

B. SERIES RESONANCE

11.1. CMOS TWO-INVERTERS—4009

The schematic of this series-resonant oscillator at 200 kHz is shown in Fig. 11.1. This circuit is a variation of the TTL inverter oscillator shown in Fig. 11.3a. Because of the longer time delay in a CMOS inverter, this CMOS version is restricted to frequencies below 300 kHz. The CMOS inverter used is the 4009, a high-current driver with a short internal time delay. There is a large variation in this inverter's time delay among different manufacturers. The RCA 4009 had the shortest time delay of any of the brands tested and is recommended.

Each inverter in Fig. 11.1 has negative feedback around it to ensure that it is biased in the middle of its linear region, so that oscillation will always start when power is applied. The feedback resistor around the first inverter is divided into two series resistors, and the center point is bypassed to ground. R_L is used as the crystal's load resistor and set equal to or somewhat less than the crystal's internal series resistance R_s.

Figure 11.1 shows good waveforms at the crystal. The small spikes on

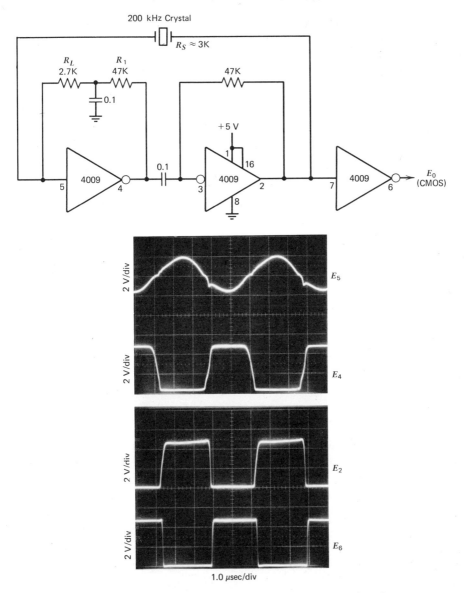

Figure 11.1. CMOS Two-Inverters (4009) circuit at 200 kHz.

the crystal's sine wave output appear to be due to the sharp edges of the crystal's square wave drive feeding through on the crystal's shunt terminal capacitance C_0.

The overall performance of the 4009 inverter circuit is poor, because its frequency is much too sensitive to changes in power supply voltage and ambient temperature.

11.2.   CMOS TWO-INVERTERS—74C04

The schematic of this series-resonant circuit at 200 kHz is shown in Fig. 11.2. The purpose of this circuit is to see if the 74C series works any better than the 4000 series, and the answer is yes, it does. The circuit in Fig. 11.2 is the same as the 4009 circuit in Fig. 11.1 except for the substitution of the 74C04 for the 4009. The 74C04 will oscillate at a higher frequency (up to 500 kHz, as compared with 300 kHz for the 4009), and it is less sensitive to temperature changes.

As in the 4009 circuit, the crystal's load resistance R_L is set equal to or somewhat less than the crystal's internal series resistance R_s. Figure 11.2 shows good waveforms at the crystal. The spikes on the crystal's sine wave output appear to be due to sharp edges of the crystal's square wave drive feeding through on the crystal's shunt terminal capacitance C_0.

The overall performance of the 74C04 inverter circuit is below average, because its frequency sensitivity to power supply voltage changes is higher than it should be. This high sensitivity to power supply voltage changes seems to be characteristic of most CMOS ICs.

11.3.   TTL TWO-INVERTERS—7404

The schematic of this series-resonant oscillator is shown in Fig. 11.3a. Many versions of this circuit are poorly designed; credit for this properly designed version of the TTL inverter circuit goes to S. D. Culp [19]. The circuit gives good performance. Crystal waveforms are fairly good, and the frequency is relatively insensitive to power supply and temperature changes. This circuit, in its many variations, is one of the most widely used TTL oscillator circuits.

The circuit uses two negative feedback schemes to ensure oscillation start-up when power is applied, one on each inverter. The circuit will work with any standard TTL NAND gate, NOR gate, or inverter. The output of each gate (or inverter) must be the negative of its input, so that negative feedback can be used to bias the input and ensure oscillator start-up. This subject is discussed in detail in Chapter 9.

The negative feedback on the second inverter in Fig. 11.3a is the simplest, consisting of the single resistor R_2. Although it does not hurt the second inverter, the single resistor feedback method has the disadvantage of reflecting back a highly nonlinear load resistance to the input (pin 3) of the inverter. A TTL inverter has a gain of approximately 10X. During transition intervals, the 470-Ω resistance of the feedback resistor R_2 is reduced to 47 Ω, as seen at the inverter's input (pin 3). At either of the binary states "0" or "1," amplifier gain is effectively zero, so the

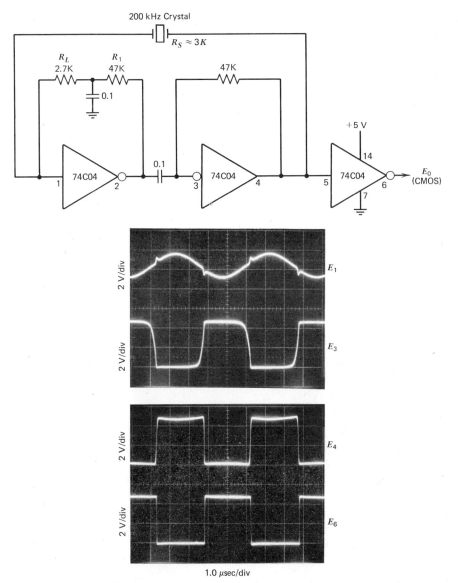

Figure 11.2. CMOS Two-Inverters (74C04) circuit at 200 kHz. (74C04 Copyright 1981 National Semiconductor Corporation.)

input impedance of the 470-Ω feedback resistor is then 470 Ω instead of 47 Ω. Such a highly nonlinear load on the amplifier input, switching back and forth between 470 and 47 Ω, is undesirable as a crystal load and it should not be used on the first inverter because of distortion introduced on the voltage output from the crystal.

The negative feedback around the first inverter is arranged differ-

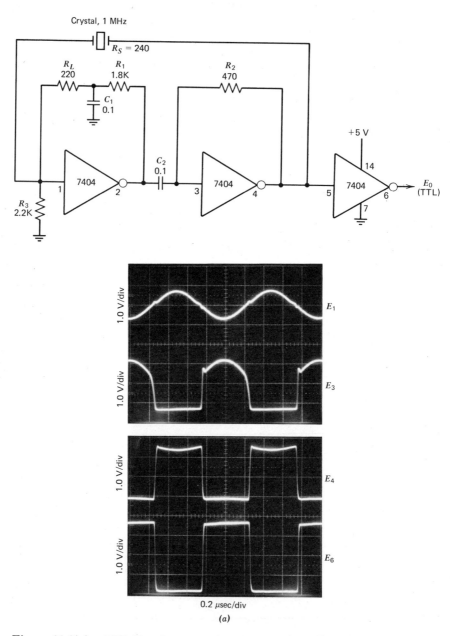

Figure 11.3(a). TTL Two-Inverters (7404) circuit at 1 MHz. Set $R_L \cong R_s$ ($R_L + R_1$) $\cong$ 2K Ω.

ently. Here, the feedback resistor is divided into two resistors R_L and R_1, and the center point is bypassed to ground with a capacitor. The resistance of the feedback network reflected back to the crystal is then constant over a complete waveform cycle and equal to R_L. The improvement in the crystal's output waveform by adding the bypass capacitor C_1 in the middle of the two feedback resistors R_L and R_1 is quite significant.

The input (pin 1) of the first inverter is also tied to ground by a resistor R_3. This shunt resistor R_3 has two functions. First, it pulls the inverter's input into the transition region, so that both the input and output of the inverter are somewhere near +1.6 VDC. The two feedback resistors (R_L and R_1) then provide additional negative feedback at low frequencies to stabilize the inverter's output voltage (pin 2) at +1.6 VDC, the binary switching point. The second function of R_3 is to control the on/off ratio of the oscillator's square wave output. Adjusting the value of R_3 (±30% ?) will trim the square wave output to a perfect 50/50 on/off ratio. The capacitor C_2 between the two inverters is used for DC isolation and allows them to be independently biased without interaction.

The small spikes on E_1 in Fig. 11.3a are high-frequency edges of the crystal's square wave drive, which are feeding through the crystal on its terminal shunt capacitance C_0. There are flat spots adjacent to the switching spikes on the crystal's output voltage E_1. These flat spots indicate that the input resistance of the inverter itself becomes very low during these flat-spot intervals. These nonlinear, low-resistance flat spots in E_1 occur at the worst possible place in the cycle, that is, at the switching point. They increase timing uncertainty as to when the inverter will switch from one binary state to the other and degrade the circuit's short-term frequency stability.

Figure 11.3b shows the inverter circuit with the 74S04 instead of the 7404, and Fig. 11.3c shows the inverter circuit with the 74LS04. The 74LS04 is the most useful of the three inverters because it covers a wider frequency range than the other two. The 74LS04's higher input resistance allows the use of larger feedback resistors. This permits a higher crystal load resistance R_L, which is needed for operation at lower frequencies. The 74LS04 will operate down to 100 kHz, whereas the 7404 will operate down to only 800 kHz, and the 74S04 down to 1 MHz. Dissipation in the crystal limits the highest oscillation frequency to about 3 MHz in all three circuits.

11.4. TTL VOLTAGE COMPARATOR—LM319

The schematic of this series-resonant circuit at 1 MHz is shown in Fig. 11.4. This circuit's performance is below average. The LM319 is the

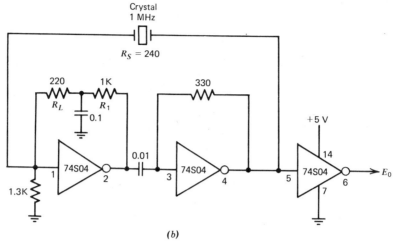

Figure 11.3(b). TTL Two-Inverters (74S04) circuit. Set $R_L \cong R_s$, $(R_L + R_1) \cong$ 1.2K Ω.

fastest of the two voltage comparators (LM319 and LM339) currently available for operation from a single +5 VDC supply. The (+) input terminal is referenced to +2.5 VDC. $R_1 C_1$ provides negative feedback at low frequencies to hold the comparator's DC output in the middle of its transition range in order to ensure oscillation at start-up.

Waveforms at the crystal are reasonable, but the crystal's load resistance R_L of 510 Ω is higher than it should be at 1 MHz with respect to the crystal's internal series resistance of 240 Ω. This is due to the amplifier's high output impedance, which is too high for good operation at 1 MHz. If

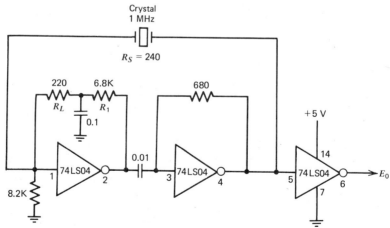

Figure 11.3(c). TTL Two-Inverters (74LS04) circuit. Set $R_L \cong R_s$, $(R_L + R_1) \cong$ 7K Ω.

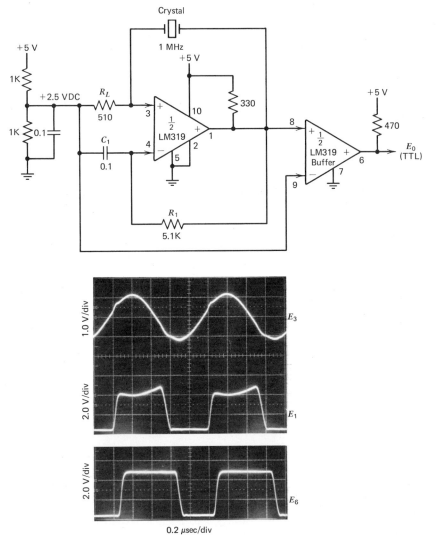

Figure 11.4. TTL voltage comparator (LM319) at 1 MHz. (LM319 Copyright 1981 National Semiconductor Corporation.)

the crystal's load resistance R_L is made lower than 510 Ω, the crystal-drive waveform E_1 becomes even more distorted than is shown in Fig. 11.4. At 500 kHz and below, the crystal's internal series resistance R_s and its load resistance R_L are both higher, and the crystal loading and drive waveform problems improve considerably.

The comparator's input impedance is highly nonlinear. This would warp the crystal's sine wave output much more than is shown in Fig. 11.4 if it were not for the linearizing effect of the crystal's load resistor R_L, which is effectively in parallel with the comparator's input impedance. This nonlinear loading effect will show up more at lower frequencies, where the desired crystal load resistance R_L is higher. Waveforms in Fig. 11.4 show about an 80-nsec time delay in the LM319 comparator, which limits it to frequencies below 500 kHz for good oscillator operation. But the nonlinear loading effects that occur at these lower frequencies mean that the LM319 will not work well as an oscillator at any frequency. An additional drawback is that the circuit continues to oscillate at a spurious frequency when the crystal is removed.

11.5.   TTL RECEIVER—9615

The circuit of this oscillator at 1 MHz is shown in Fig. 11.5. The circuit gives above-average performance. Both receiver inputs are internally biased at +1.9 VDC. R_1C_1 provides negative feedback at low frequencies to servo the output at pin 1 to +1.9 VDC, approximately in the middle of the transition region, in order to ensure oscillation at start-up. Waveforms at the crystal are very good. The frequency is not very sensitive to power supply or temperature changes. The crystal's load resistance R_L is set equal to or somewhat less than the crystal's internal series resistance R_s.

The circuit uses very few parts and will operate from 100 kHz to 2 MHz. There are two 9615 receivers in a DIP, and the second one makes a convenient isolating buffer for the oscillator.

11.6.   TTL RECEIVER—8820

The schematic for this oscillator at 1 MHz is shown in Fig. 11.6. R_2 biases the negative (−) input terminal (pin 1) to approximately the same +2.5 VDC bias point as the positive (+) input terminal. R_1C_1 applies negative feedback at low frequencies to hold DC output at the midpoint of the transition region in order to ensure oscillation at startup.

Waveforms at the crystal are fairly good. The output impedance of the 8820 at pin 6 is too high to properly drive a 1-MHz crystal, and so the tops of the E_6 square wave curve downward as the crystal's sine wave of current flows back into its driving source at pin 6. Because of this, the crystal's load resistance, which consists of R_L and the 8820's input resistance of 2.5K Ω in parallel, is not so low as desired. With $R_L = 1K\ \Omega$, the net crystal load is 715 Ω, which is about 3 times higher than the crystal's

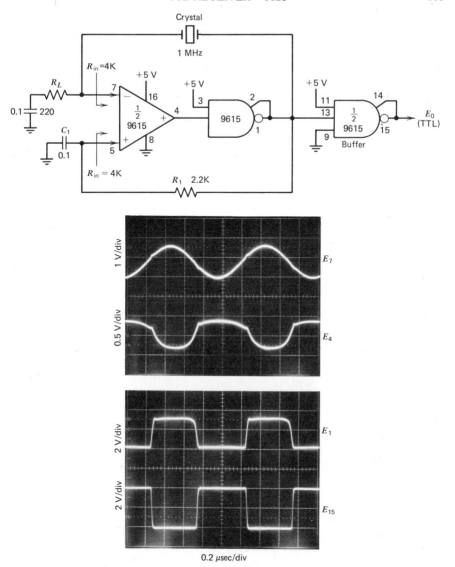

Figure 11.5. TTL receiver (9615) at 1 mHz. (9615 Courtesy Fairchild Camera and Instrument Corporation.)

internal series resistance of 240 Ω. This reduces the circuit's short-term frequency stability.

The waveform of the square wave driving the crystal would look better at frequencies of 500 kHz or lower, where the crystal's internal series resistance R_s is higher. The waveforms show about a 70-nsec time delay in the 8820 line receiver.

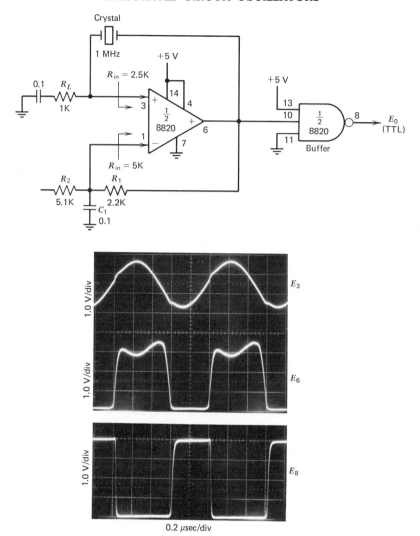

Figure 11.6. TTL receiver (8820) at 1 mHz. (8820 Copyright 1981 National Semiconductor Corporation.)

11.7. ECL RECEIVER—10114

The schematic of this series-resonant oscillator at 1 MHz is shown in Fig. 11.7*a* and the circuit waveforms in Fig. 11.7*b*. This circuit has outstanding performance and works very nicely off a +5 VDC supply. Waveforms at the crystal are very good, equal to the best of any circuit tested. The frequency changes very little when power supply voltage or temperature is changed. The low ECL drive voltage keeps crystal dissipation low.

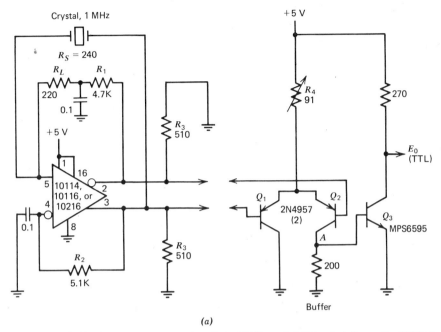

(a)

Figure 11.7(a). Series-resonant circuit in ECL at 1 MHz. Set $R_L \cong R_s$. (10114, 10116, 10216 Courtesy Motorola, Inc.)

And the low ECL drive resistance means the crystal can have a low load resistance R_L, which gives very good short-term frequency stability.

The ECL receiver format is well-adapted to high-frequency oscillator circuits. At high frequencies, crystals are low impedance devices, and ECL circuits can drive low impedance loads down to 50 Ω easily. Input resistances of ECL circuits are high, and they are also linear over the ECL voltage range. As shown in Fig. 11.7b, the crystal's square wave drive waveform at pin 3 has a definite slope during transitions between binary states, indicating the ECL unit is operating as a linear amplifier during the transition interval.

The 10114, 10116, and 10216 are similar in that they have the same pin connections and are directly interchangeable in the circuit in Fig. 11.7a. They differ slightly in speed and internal construction. All three have the required push-pull inputs and outputs needed for an ECL oscillator. The 10216 has the widest bandwidth and should be used at the highest frequencies (4–20 MHz). The 10116 has medium bandwidth and should be used at medium frequencies (1–6 MHz). The 10114 has the least bandwidth and should be used at lower frequencies (500 kHz–4 MHz).

Figure 11.7c shows the circuit at 20 MHz. The crystal's internal series

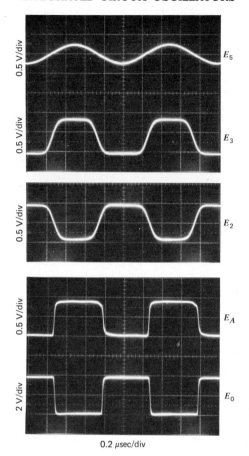

Figure 11.7(b).   Waveforms for series-resonant-ECL circuit in Fig. 11.7a.

resistance R_s is 7 Ω; the crystal's load resistance R_L is 10 Ω. At 20 MHz, the ECL receiver has to be able to drive a 17-Ω load ($R_s + R_L = 17\ \Omega$), a very low value. The receiver's output resistance is controlled by the ECL emitter's output current, which is, in turn, controlled by the emitter's pulldown resistor R_3. $R_3 = 510\ \Omega$ works well at 1 MHz, but it has to decrease to 100 Ω at 20 MHz to get the ECL output resistance down low enough to provide a reasonable drive waveform to the crystal.

There are three ECL receivers in one DIP. One of the two unused ones could be used as a no-cost buffer between the oscillator and the two-transistor buffer, but the circuit will oscillate spuriously when the crystal is removed. Because of this, the ECL receivers are not used as buffers.

The buffer circuit is specifically designed to minimize capacitive loading (the Miller effect) from the buffer onto the oscillator, which can

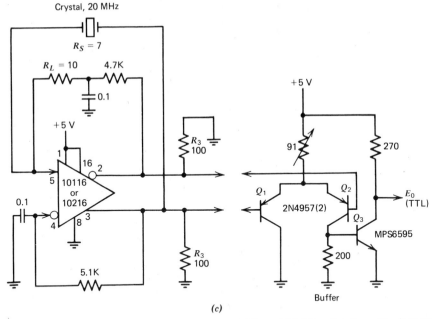

Figure 11.7(c). Series-resonant circuit in ECL at 20 MHz. Set $R_L \cong R_s$. (10116, 10216 Courtesy Motorola, Inc.)

change the oscillation frequency. Part of the buffer design shown in Fig. 11.7a is taken from Blood [20]. To minimize the Miller capacitance effect, Q_1 is operated without a collector load resistor, and the voltage swing at the collector of Q_2 is limited to 0.7 V peak by the base-emitter junction of Q_3. The square wave on/off ratio at the output of Q_3 depends on the gain of Q_3, which varies from one transistor to the next. The on/off ratio at the output also depends on R_4. Making R_4 adjustable provides an adjustment of the on/off ratio at the output if it is needed.

C. PIERCE

11.8. CMOS INVERTER—74C04

The circuit of this Pierce-IC oscillator at 1 MHz is shown in Fig. 11.8. The output resistance R_0 of the first inverter is used as the integrating resistor for the $R_0 C_2$ phase-lag network. Small values of C_1 and C_2 are used in order to minimize the gain reduction they introduce. One result of this is that the crystal oscillates a little higher above its series-resonant frequency. R_1 provides negative DC feedback around the inverter in order to put it in the linear region so that oscillation will start when

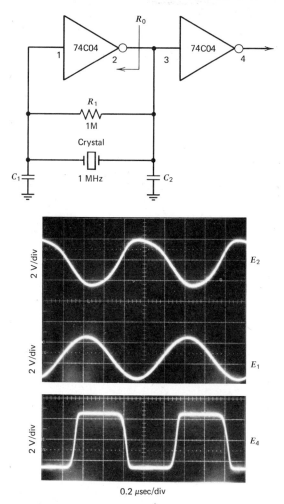

Figure 11.8. Pierce in CMOS (74C04). (74C04 Copyright 1981 National Semiconductor Corporation.) At a frequency of 1 MHz, C_1 and C_2 = 220 pF; at a frequency of 2 MHz, C_1 and C_2 = 330 pF. For Solid State Scientific's 4000A/B series only, at a frequency of 5 MHz, C_1 = 330 pF and C_2 = 100 pF.

power is applied. The second inverter squares up the output waveform and also acts as an isolation buffer.

This CMOS circuit works reasonably well at frequencies up to 1 MHz. Above 1 MHz, variations among manufacturers show up, and only certain brands will work satisfactorily. National Semiconductor's 74C series will work up to 2 MHz, and Solid State Scientific's 4000A/B series will work up to 5 MHz. Capacitance values of C_1 and C_2 at 1, 2, and 5 MHz are listed in Fig. 11.8. Above 2 MHz, the crystal's dissipation should be checked, so that its dissipation limit is not exceeded.

11.9. TTL VOLTAGE COMPARATOR—LM319

The schematic of this Pierce-IC at 1 MHz is shown in Fig. 11.9. The LM319 is a voltage comparator with a relatively large 60-nsec internal time delay, which limits its upper oscillation frequency to about 2 MHz. There are faster comparators available, but they require ±15 V power rather than only +5 V. The LM319's high input impedance allows it to operate at frequencies down to 10 kHz. Its input impedance is quite nonlinear, however, which will distort the crystal's output waveform at lower frequencies. R_2 and R_3 provide a DC feedback to ensure that the comparator is in its linear conducting region and will start oscillating when power is applied.

The LM319 performs well as a Pierce oscillator. The 50-Ω reactive impedance of the 3300-pF capacitor C_2 (at 1 MHz) swamps out the LM319's nonlinear input impedance, and the voltage waveforms at the crystal are reasonably good. The on/off ratio at the output can be adjusted closer to 50/50 than is shown in the waveform photograph by adjusting the ratio of the biasing resistors R_4 and R_5. The circuit does have the disadvantage that it oscillates spuriously with the crystal out of the circuit. There are two LM319 comparators in a DIP, and for convenience, the second one is used as an isolation amplifier.

11.10. ECL RECEIVER—10114

A schematic of this Pierce-IC at 1 MHz is shown in Fig. 11.10a and its waveforms in Fig. 11.10b. Three ECL receiver stages are cascaded to provide the high gain required by the Pierce circuit. The circuit works well at 1 MHz with the 10114, but not with the 10116. R_2 and R_3 provide DC feedback around the receivers to bias them into the linear operating region, so that the circuit will start oscillating when power is applied.

Frequency stability with both power supply and temperature changes is very good; crystal waveforms are also reasonably good. One drawback to the circuit is the fairly large number of discrete parts required. The buffer circuit converts the oscillator's ECL output to a TTL format. The buffer is designed to minimize capacitive loading effects on the oscillator circuit. The design of the buffer is discussed in more detail in Section 11.7.

Figure 11.10c shows the same circuit at 20 MHz. Either the 10116 or the 10216 can be used at this frequency, but not the 10114, which does not have enough gain at 20 MHz for the circuit to oscillate. This circuit

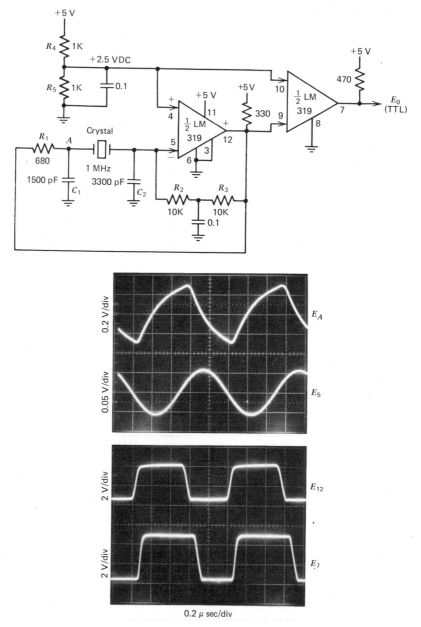

Figure 11.9. Pierce in TTL (LM319) at 1 MHz. (LM319 Copyright 1981 National Semiconductor Corporation.)

176

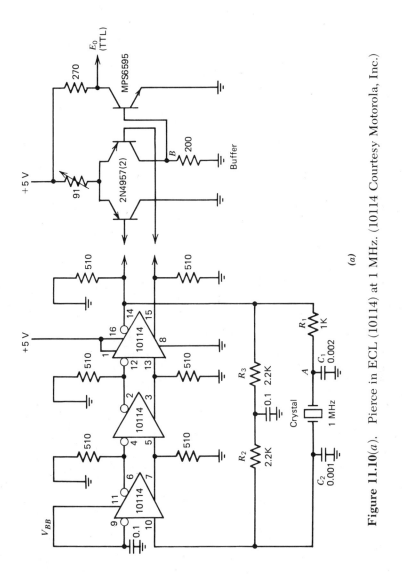

Figure 11.10(a). Pierce in ECL (10114) at 1 MHz. (10114 Courtesy Motorola, Inc.)

177

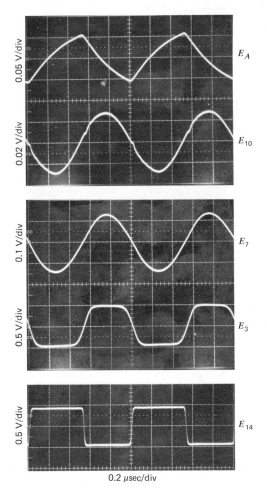

Figure 11.10(b).   Waveforms for Pierce-ECL circuit in Fig. 11.10a.

gives good performance and has good waveforms at the crystal. Note that
the output resistance of the ECL stage that drives the crystal has been
lowered by decreasing emitter-pulldown resistors R_4 to 200 Ω, so it can
drive the low resistance crystal load at 20 MHz. The frequency sensitivity of the 10116 to power supply changes is only half that of the 10216.
The 10116 oscillates spuriously when the crystal is removed from the
circuit, but the 10216 does not. For best short-term frequency stability,
C_2 should be four times larger than the 470 pF shown in Fig. 11.10c, but
the circuit does not have enough gain to permit the additional gain loss
involved in doing this. Circuit layout is important in this circuit to prevent spurious oscillation.

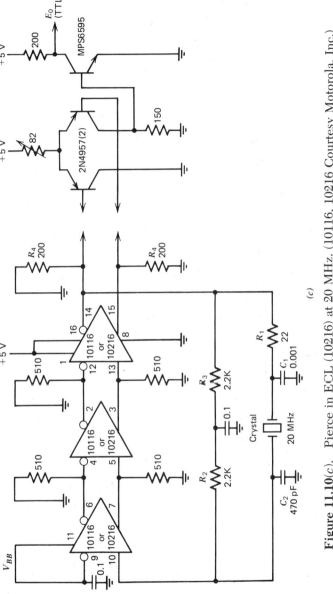

Figure 11.10(c). Pierce in ECL (10216) at 20 MHz. (10116, 10216 Courtesy Motorola, Inc.)

(c)

D. MEACHAM

11.11. MEACHAM—10114

As an IC oscillator, the Meacham circuit's needs for both positive (+) and negative (−) bridge drive signals effectively limits it to ECL. An ECL receiver has both (+) and (−) inputs and outputs and provides an opportunity to try Meacham's full-bridge rather than only the half-bridge circuit. A schematic of Meacham's full-bridge circuit at 10 MHz is shown in Fig. 11.11a; it is a complex circuit with good performance. Figure 11.11b shows voltage waveforms at several points in the circuit in Fig. 11.11a.

The 10114 works well in this circuit, but not the 10116 or the 10216. The amplifier uses two ECL stages, giving a gain of 18X from point A to pin 14. If three ECL stages are used, the amplifier becomes unstable and oscillates parasitically at 60 MHz. Emitter-pulldown resistors at the ECL amplifier's output are set to give maximum emitter current, which gives the lowest possible output resistance. This is needed to drive the crystal's low internal series resistance R_s of 5 Ω.

C_3 and C_4 permit negative feedback at DC, stabilizing the bias point and ensuring that oscillation will start when power is applied. C_2 balances out the crystal's shunt terminal capacitance C_0, which helps minimize parasitic oscillation.

The bridge excitation is a square wave. The resonant L_1C_1 tank selects the fundamental sine wave from the bridge output, ignores the harmonics, and reduces the response at frequencies away from resonance. R_1 reduces the L_1C_1 phase shift from 90° down to 0° at frequencies far away from resonance. R_3 isolates L_1C_1 from the crystal. The waveform clean-up by the L_1C_1 tank can be seen in E_2 (waveform at pin 2), which is proportional to the differential input signal between pins 4 and 5 in Fig. 11.11a. The peculiar looking waveform E_A out of the bridge at point A is normal and occurs when a square wave with sloping sides (through bridge arm R_2) is subtracted from a sine wave (through the crystal arm).

The minimum theoretical value for R_2 is equal to the crystal's internal series resistance R_s of 5 Ω. The minimum practical value for R_2 measures 8.2 Ω, which gives a practical to theoretical minimum ratio of 8.2/5 or 1.6 for R_2.

Meacham's full-bridge circuit can be changed into the modified Meacham half-bridge circuit shown in Fig. 11.11c. The isolation resistor R_3 is increased to 240 Ω to compensate for the drop in bridge source resistance when the two 240-Ω bridge arms are removed. The performance of the half-bridge circuit is just as good as that of the full-bridge

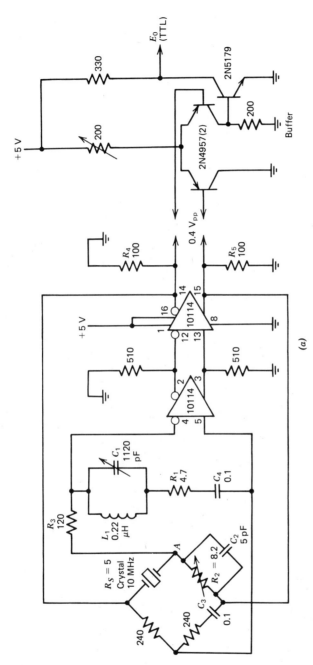

Figure 11.11(a). Meacham at 10 MHz. (10114 Courtesy Motorola, Inc.)

181

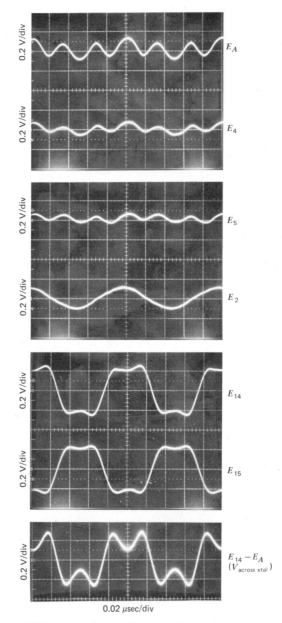

Figure 11.11(b). Waveforms for Meacham circuit in Fig. 11.11a.

182

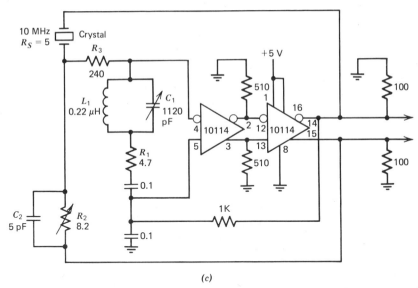

(c)

Figure 11.11(c). Modified Meacham at 10 MHz. (10114 Courtesy Motorola, Inc.)

circuit, as far as could be measured. The minimum practical value for R_2 in the half-bridge circuit is also 8.2 Ω, which gives the same ratio of 8.2/5 or 1.6 for R_2. The full-bridge circuit does cancel out source resistance variations in the bridge drive, so its frequency stability is potentially better than that of the half-bridge circuit. The short-term stability of both circuits measured 0.1 ppm, at the limit of available measuring equipment. The full-bridge circuit is preferred to the half-bridge; the only advantage of the half-bridge circuit is that it uses one less resistor than the full-bridge circuit.

E. SPECIAL OSCILLATOR ICs

11.12. CMOS 7209

The schematic of this Pierce-IC oscillator at 10 MHz is shown in Fig. 11.12. The 7209 uses a single CMOS inverter in the oscillator circuit and has an internal feedback resistor around the inverter to bias the input into its linear conducting region and ensure oscillator start-up when power is applied. The advantage of the 7209 is that it will oscillate at frequencies up to 10 MHz, while an ordinary CMOS inverter quits at 2–5 MHz in the Pierce circuit (see Section 11.8). The oscillator and its fundamental frequency output will operate at frequencies down to at least 4 kHz.

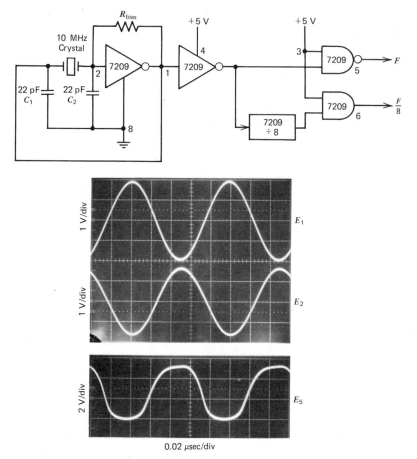

Figure 11.12. 7209 at 10 MHz. (7209 Reproduced by permission of Intersil, Inc. from Data Sheet ICM 7209 CMOS Clock Generator. Copyright 1979 Intersil, Inc. All rights reserved.)

The 7209 provides a second output frequency at ⅛ the crystal frequency. This divide-by-eight output uses dynamic divider circuitry, which will operate at 2 MHz (crystal frequency) with a 5 V supply voltage. The divide-by-eight circuit will work at crystal frequencies lower than 2 MHz by reducing the supply voltage below 5 V. When the crystal is removed from the circuit, the fundamental frequency output stops (as it should), but the dynamic divide-by-eight frequency output at pin 6 continues to free run at a spurious frequency.

The 7209 gives reasonably good performance at both 1 and 10 MHz. At 1 MHz, it operates over a wide range of supply voltage and temperature. At 10 MHz, the supply voltage must be greater than +4 V, and the temperature rise above ambient must be somewhat less than what is permissible at 1 MHz, or the output voltage swing at pin 5 will drop to zero.

In a Pierce circuit, the values of the two capacitors C_1 and C_2 should be changed when the frequency is changed. At 1 MHz, both C_1 and C_2 in Fig. 11.12 should be 100 pF. And at 100 kHz, both C_1 and C_2 should be 470 pF.

The 10-MHz waveform photographs in Fig. 11.12 show that voltage across the crystal is 2.4 Vrms, while Fig. 2.5 shows that maximum crystal voltage at series resonance is 0.3 Vrms at 10 MHz. Is the crystal's 2-mW dissipation limit being exceeded? The answer is no, because the crystal is operating inductively, way above series resonance. The current through the crystal can be determined from the voltage drop across the crystal load. Figure 11.12 shows 1.4 Vrms across a total capacitive load of about 32 pF (22 pF plus 5 pF stray plus 5-pF amplifier input capacitance). At 10 MHz, 32 pF has an impedance of 520 Ω, which gives a crystal current of $1.4/520 = 2.7$ mA rms. Figure 2.3 shows a maximum crystal series resistance R_s of 25 Ω at 10 MHz. Calculating the crystal's power dissipation from I^2R_s gives 0.18 mW, which is less than the crystal's 2-mW dissipation limit.

11.13.   TTL 74LS321

The 74LS321 uses a variation of the common base amplifier circuit, and a brief schematic at 1 MHz is shown in Fig. 11.13. The 74LS321 operates over a frequency range of 1–20 MHz and is the oscillator section of the 74LS362. The 74LS320 is identical to the 74LS321 except that the divide-by-two and the divide-by-four frequency outputs have been deleted in the 74LS320.

The source and load resistances seen by the crystal looking back into the circuit at pins 14 and 15 both measure 40 Ω, giving the crystal an external load resistance of 80 Ω. The inductor L_1, together with the collector resistor R_1, provides a phase-lead network in the oscillator loop. The inductance value to be used for L_1 varies with frequency, and the circuit will not oscillate unless the proper inductance value is used. Table 11.1 lists inductance values recommended by the manufacturer at various frequencies. From a design point of view, it is not necessary to use an inductor to make a common base amplifier circuit operate as a fundamental oscillator over the 1–20-MHz frequency range. The inductor is apparently carried over from the 74LS362 design, where it was needed to provide an LC tank for harmonic operation at 48 MHz.

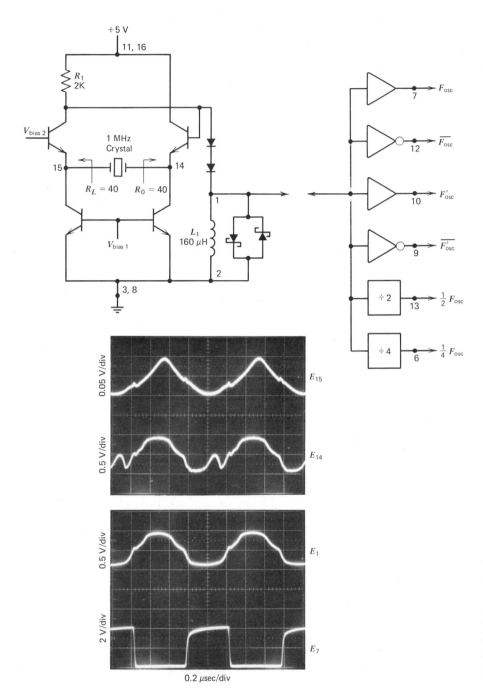

Figure 11.13. 74LS321 at 1 MHz. (74LS321 Courtesy Texas Instruments Incorporated.)

186

TABLE 11.1

Inductance to Be Used in the 74LS321 Circuit
at Various Frequencies

Frequency (MHz)	Inductance L_1 (μH)
1	160.
2	100.
3	59.
4	37.
5	24.
6	16.5
7	11.
8	8.5
9	7.
10	6.
15	5.5
20	5.

This circuit does not perform very well; the voltage waveform driving the crystal is poor. At 1 MHz, the frequency is reasonably stable and changes only 4 ppm when the power supply voltage is changed from 4 to 6 V. But at 20 MHz, the frequency drifts 1 ppm short termwise and changes 102 ppm when the power supply voltage is changed from 4 to 6 V.

11.14. TTL SP705B

A schematic of this circuit at 1 MHz is shown in Fig. 11.14. The SP705B uses the common base amplifier circuit and is designed for frequencies up to 10 MHz. No minimum frequency is specified by the manufacturer, but the crystal's internal series resistance R_s is specified at 300 Ω maximum, which corresponds to a minimum frequency of about 1 MHz.

Looking back into the circuit at pin 6, the source resistance R_0 driving the crystal is 110 Ω, and looking back into the circuit at pin 5, the crystal's load resistance R_L is 32 Ω. This gives a total resistive load on the crystal of 142 Ω. This is a reasonable load value at 1 MHz, where the crystal's internal series resistance R_s is 240 Ω, and gives fairly good in-circuit Q and short-term frequency stability at 1 MHz. But 142 Ω is too high a load resistance at 10 MHz, where the crystal's internal series resistance is about 15 Ω. This high load resistance reduces both the crystal's in-circuit Q and the short-term frequency stability at higher frequencies.

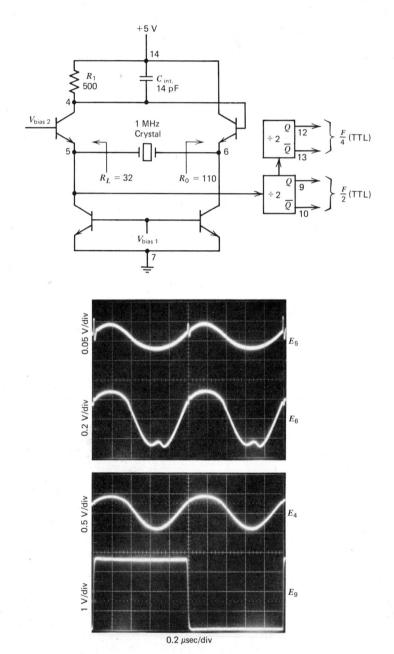

Figure 11.14. SP705B at 1 MHz. (SP705B Courtesy Plessey Semiconductors.)

188

At 1 MHz, it takes the circuit about 1 second to start oscillating, but at 10 MHz, it starts immediately. Only the half-frequency and quarter-frequency outputs have a TTL format. The crystal's fundamental frequency is available at pin 6, but it is a low voltage signal (0.6 Vp-p) and will not drive TTL circuitry directly.

The circuit's performance is fair at 1 MHz but poor at 10 MHz. Waveforms at the crystal are poor; the driving waveform is distorted, and the output waveform shows a pair of switching spikes riding on top of the waveform. At 1 MHz, the oscillation frequency is relatively insensitive to temperature and power supply voltage changes. But at 10 MHz, the frequency shifts 47 ppm when the power supply voltage changes from 4 to 6 V.

11.15. ECL 12061

A schematic of this IC oscillator is shown in Fig. 11.15. This oscillator uses a variation of the common base amplifier circuit and incorporates an AGC (automatic gain control) loop to keep oscillation amplitude at a low level and minimize power dissipation in the crystal. The oscillator has three outputs: sine wave, ECL, and TTL and comes in two frequency ranges: the 12060 for a 100 kHz–2 MHz operation and the 12061 for a 2–20 MHz operation. In the 12060, the source and load resistances seen by the crystal looking back into pins 5 and 6 are both 2.7K Ω, giving a total crystal load resistance of 5.4K Ω. In the 12061, the source and load resistances looking back into pins 5 and 6 are both 130 Ω, giving a total crystal load resistance of 260 Ω. A 0.1-μF bypass capacitor is required directly across the oscillator section's power pins from pin 1 to pin 8 to minimize noise coupling into the oscillator. If the TTL output section is used, a second 0.1-μF capacitor is required directly across its power pins from pin 9 to pin 11 to minimize noise coupling of the TTL switching transients into the oscillator section.

Unfortunately, neither the 12060 nor the 12061 work very well, particularly at the high-frequency ends of their range. Crystal waveforms are poor; the 2-MHz waveforms shown in Fig. 11.15 for the 12061 are typical of either IC at any frequency. The 12060 is reasonably insensitive to power supply and temperature changes at 100 kHz. But at its upper frequency limit of 2 MHz, the frequency is unstable with temperature and shifts 150–180 ppm when heated or cooled above or below ambient. The 12061 works reasonably well at its low frequency limit of 2 MHz, but at its upper frequency limit of 20 MHz, there is a relatively large

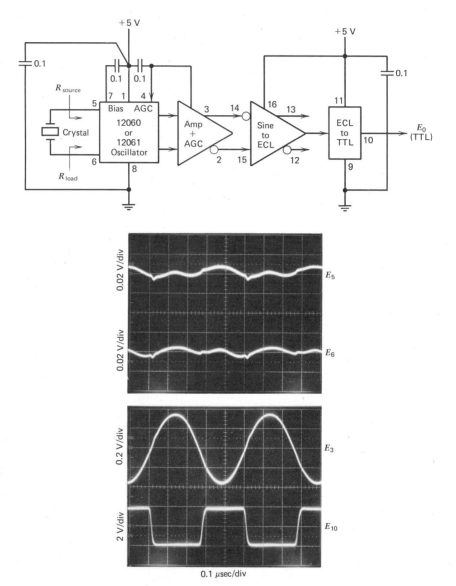

Figure 11.15. 12060, 12061 circuit. Waveforms are for the 12061 at 2 MHz. (12060, 12061 Courtesy Motorola, Inc.)

190

14-ppm frequency shift when the power supply voltage is changed from 4 to 6 V and a large 28-ppm frequency shift when heated above ambient. The basic difficulty seems to be that IC source and load resistances seen by the crystal are scaled for operation at the low end of each frequency range and are too large to operate well at the high end.

11.16. LINEAR LM375

A schematic of this series-resonant circuit at 500 kHz is shown in Fig. 11.16a. The LM375 contains two buffer amplifiers and provides both sine wave and TTL outputs. A sine wave rather than a square wave can be obtained from the first buffer by interchanging its input leads and disconnecting the TTL driver. The LM375 oscillator section contains a very wideband amplifier, with a relatively high output resistance at pin 5. Because of the amplifier's wide bandwidth, it is necessary to add capacitor C_1 across the oscillator's input at the lower frequencies (500 kHz), as shown in Fig. 11.16a, in order to avoid extra noise switchings when the oscillator's waveform switches polarity.

With a resistive load R_2 on the oscillator, the highest oscillation frequency is limited to about 500 kHz because of loading effects on the oscillator's high output resistance. Above 500 kHz, the amplifier's square wave output gets too distorted to drive a low resistance crystal.

The LM375 can be used at frequencies up to 10 MHz if a tuned LC tank instead of the resistor R_2 is used for the oscillator load. Figure 11.16b shows a circuit for 10 MHz operation. The crystal is tapped down on the LC tank in order to raise the crystal's low internal resistance R_s to a much higher value, as seen by the amplifier's output at pin 5. Tapping down the crystal on the LC tank has a considerable effect on the circuit, and this is discussed in detail in Sections 5.13 and 7.6.

The oscillator section of the LM375 will work at up to 60 MHz, but the buffer and TTL driver circuits will not operate properly above 10 MHz. From a general design viewpoint, it is not necessary to use an LC tank for fundamental operation at 10 MHz, but it is needed here because the oscillator's high output resistance needs a high load impedance to work into.

The oscillator performs well with a resistive oscillator load at and below 500 kHz. Crystal waveforms are good, and the oscillation frequency is relatively independent of power supply and temperature changes.

The oscillator gives only a fair performance with a resonant LC tank

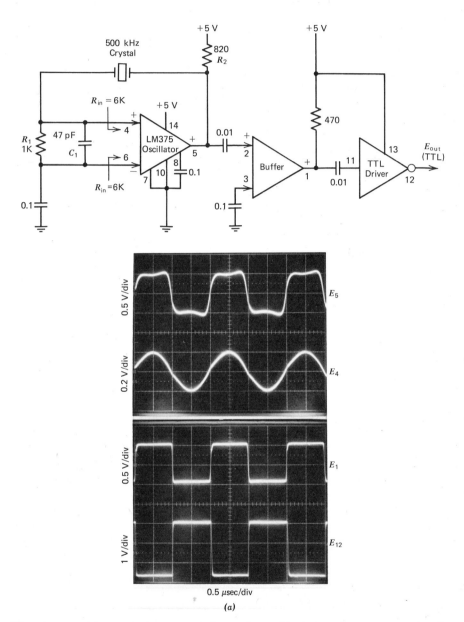

Figure 11.16(*a*). LM375 at 500 kHz. (LM375 Copyright 1981 National Semiconductor Corporation.)

192

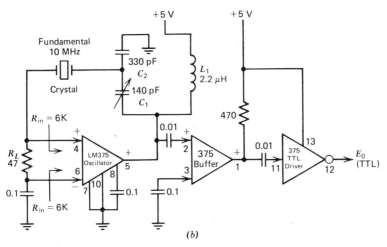

Figure 11.16(b). LM375 at 10 MHz. (LM375 Copyright 1981 National Semiconductor Corporation.)

for the oscillator load. The crystal's load resistance R_L at 10 MHz should be about 10 Ω or less but could not be reduced below 33 Ω without starting parasitic oscillations. In addition, the circuit oscillates spuriously when the crystal is removed from the circuit. The LM375 has been discontinued by the manufacturer.

11.17. LINEAR SL680C

A schematic of this emitter coupled circuit at 2 MHz is shown in Fig. 11.17a, and its waveforms are shown in Fig. 11.17b. The SL680C has an AGC loop to keep the crystal's power dissipation low; it has only a sine wave output, at pin 6. The emitter follower output at pin 7 should not be used, since any external noise picked up here couples directly onto the crystal, and any loading effects will reduce loop gain and may prevent the circuit from oscillating.

The power supply voltage of the SL680C is rated at +6 to +10 VDC, but it will operate at +5 V if a sine wave output with its negative peak flattened off is acceptable. Waveforms in Fig. 11.17b are for a +6 V rather than +5 V supply, in order to show the sine wave output at pin 6 when the IC is operated within its rated power supply range.

The load resistance seen by the crystal looking into pin 1 is 45 Ω. The loop gain of the emitter coupled circuit varies inversely with the crystal's internal series resistance R_s, which means that loop gain decreases as

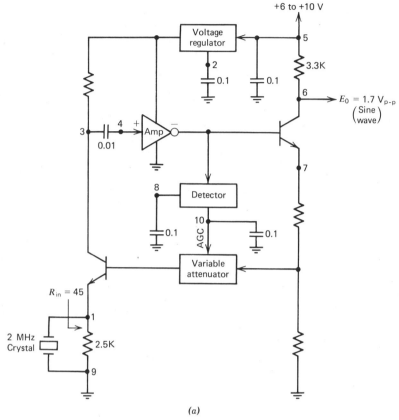

(a)

Figure 11.17(a). SL680C at 2 MHz. (SL680C Courtesy Plessey Semiconductors.)

frequency decreases. The SL680C oscillated properly at frequencies of 2–20 MHz but would not oscillate at 1 MHz or lower. It would not operate harmonically much above 20 MHz even when a parallel tuned LC circuit (AC coupled) was added from pin 4 to ground in Fig. 11.17a.

The circuit gives good performance at 2 MHz and fair performance at 20 MHz. Operating the circuit at +5 VDC rather than at +6 V makes little difference at 2 MHz other than the flattened negative peak on the sine wave output. At 20 MHz and +5 V, frequency is fairly sensitive to the power supply voltage, changing 35 ppm when the power supply voltage is dropped from +6 V to +5 VDC. The frequency shift is much less within the SL680C's rated supply range, changing only 3 ppm when the power supply voltage is changed from +6 to +8 V. Also, at 20 MHz, the frequency changes quite a bit (12 ppm) when heated above ambient regardless of whether the power supply voltage is +5 V or +8 V.

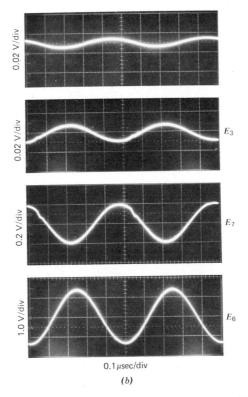

Figure 11.17(*b*).   Waveforms for SL680C circuit in Fig. 11.17*a*.

F.   VHF HARMONIC

11.18.   ECL RECEIVER—10216 (100 MHz)

This is a VHF harmonic oscillator that uses an ECL IC for its amplifier. It is a series-resonant circuit oscillating at 100 MHz, with a capacitive tap on the LC tank; the schematic is shown in Fig. 11.18. The circuit is a variation of Butler's emitter follower circuit in Fig. 5.31, with the emitter follower having a gain of 1.5–6X instead of just 1X. For frequency stability, L_1 must have an air core, while L_0 is not very critical and can have an iron core. R_1 has a big effect on circuit operation; if R_1 is too high, $L_1 C_1$ tunes so strongly that it takes control over the oscillation frequency away from the crystal. If R_1 is too low, it broadens the bandwidth of the $L_1 C_1$ tank so much that the tank loses its primary function of selecting which harmonic the crystal is to oscillate at. If R_1 is made even smaller, loop gain becomes less than 1X, and the circuit will not oscillate at all.

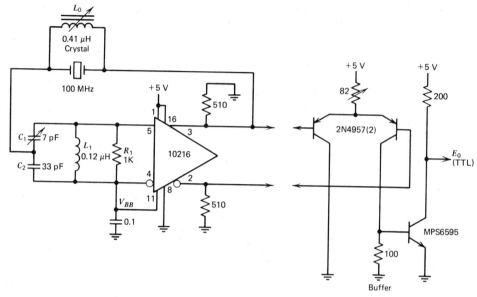

Figure 11.18. VHF harmonic oscillator in ECL (10216) at 100 MHz. (10216 Courtesy Motorola, Inc.)

This circuit works very well. Its short-term frequency stability is very good, and its sensitivity to power supply changes is low and reasonably low to temperature changes. The circuit shows no parasitic oscillation effects. The buffer is designed to minimize capacitive loading effects on the oscillator circuit. The design of the buffer is discussed in more detail in Section 11.7.

CHAPTER TWELVE

COMPARING THE CIRCUITS

This chapter describes the relative performance of all the oscillator circuits and lists their strong and weak points. To obtain the performance data, a test circuit of each type was built and its performance measured. The circuits are discussed individually, and their performance is summarized in three tables: one for discrete transistor circuits, one for ICs, and one for harmonic circuits. At the end of this chapter, the circuits are rated on a relative scale of outstanding to poor.

12.1. PERFORMANCE CRITERIA

There are several criteria for rating the performance of oscillator circuits. One important factor is whether the crystal likes the circuit, as indicated by voltage waveforms in and out of the crystal. Another important factor is the in-circuit Q, which depends on the ratio of the circuit's external resistance as seen by the crystal across its terminals to the crystal's internal series resistance R_s. The frequency should be reasonably independent of power supply and temperature changes, and power dissipation in the crystal should be low. Circuit complexity and parts count are factors to be considered. Spurious oscillations when the crystal is removed from the circuit are undesirable, as are parasitics.

12.2. OSCILLATORS USING DISCRETE TRANSISTORS

Performance of the different discrete transistor circuits varies from outstanding to poor, and is listed in Table 12.1. The data were obtained from

TABLE 12.1 Performance of Discrete Transistor Oscillator Circuits

Circuit	Schematic in Figure	Useful Frequency Range	Measured Performance	
			Does Circuit Oscillate Without Crystal?	Frequency of Oscillation (MHz)
Miller-FET	10.1a	1 kHz– 20 MHz	No	1.000 139
Miller-transistor	10.2a	500 kHz– 20 MHz	No	1.000 030
Colpitts-FET, RC	10.3a	1 kHz– 10 MHz	No	1.000 150
Colpitts-FET, LC	10.3b	1 kHz– 10 MHz	No	1.000 136
Colpitts-transistor, RC	10.4a	200 kHz– 20 MHz	No	1.000 094
Colpitts-transistor, LC	10.4b	200 kHz– 20 MHz	No	1.000 257
Low capacitance load	10.5a	100 kHz– 10 MHz	No	1.000 301
High resistance load	10.6a	100 kHz– 10 MHz	No	1.000 671
Common base-transistor	10.7b	1– 600 kHz	No	0.004 000
Common base-transistor	10.7a	1– 20 MHz	No	0.999 997
Common gate-FET	10.8	100 kHz– 1 MHz	No	0.999 997
Pierce	10.9a	1 kHz– 20 MHz	No	1.000 009
Pierce—exact series resonance	10.10a	1 kHz– 20 MHz	No	1.000 000
Pierce without series resistor	10.11a	1 kHz– 20 MHz	No	1.000 009
Pierce low frequency	10.9d	1– 500 kHz	No	0.004 000
Pierce high frequency	10.9g	5– 20 MHz	No	20.000 432
Emitter coupled	10.12	100 kHz– 20 MHz	No	0.999 998
Modified Meacham	10.13d	1 kHz– 20 MHz	No	0.100 002
Modified Meacham	10.13a	1 kHz– 20 MHz	No	1.000 000
Modified Meacham	10.13c	1 kHz– 20 MHz	No	10.000 019

Waveforms at Crystal	P.S. Sensitivity (ΔV_{cc} = 2 V) Δf (ppm)	Circuit Temperature Sensitivity		Overall Performance	Remarks
		Freeze Δf (ppm)	Heat Δf (ppm)		
Good	3.	−6.	+4.	Poor	Not recommended
Poor	9.	+3.	−4.	Poor	Not recommended
Good	0.7	+2.	−1.	Good	Low parts count
Fair	2.	+2.	−5.	Good	Useful as harmonic oscillator
Fair	3.	−1.	−0.6	Fair	Low parts count
Fair	4.	+2.	−3.	Fair	Useful as harmonic oscillator
Fair	1.	+0.6	−1.	Good	
Fair	3.	+2.	−3.	Fair	
Very good	2.	+3.	−4.	Very good	
Good	0.3	0.0	−2.	Very good	
Very good	0.1	+0.4	−5.	Very good	
Good	1.	+0.5	−2.	Best	Recommended
Very good	0.8	+2.	−2.	Best	Recommended
Fair	0.7	+0.5	−0.7	Good	
Very good	0.0	+0.1	−3.	Very good	Recommended
Very good	2.	−3.	+0.1	Good	High parts count
Good	0.5	−0.3	−0.8	Good	High parts count
Good	1.	—	—	Good	Best short-term stability
Good	0.1	−0.2	−1.	Very good	
Fair	1.	—	—	Good	

Measured Performance

the circuits in Figs. 10.1–10.13, and their performance is summarized in the following paragraphs.

Miller circuits (Figs. 10.1a and 10.2a) give poor performance. The crystal waveform is awful in the transistor circuit, and only fair in the FET circuit. The frequency is 30–139 ppm above series resonance. The frequency shifts considerably with power supply and temperature changes, and with the gain of the transistor used. In addition, the frequency is very sensitive to the feedback capacitance used.

Colpitts circuits (Figs. 10.3a–d and 10.4a–d) give average performance. The crystal waveform varies from poor to very good. The frequency is 94–257 ppm above series resonance, and is very sensitive to the value of capacitor C_2. A FET works much better in this circuit than a transistor. Colpitts circuits have very few parts, a practical advantage.

The low capacitance load circuit (Fig. 10.5a) gives average performance. The crystal waveforms are only fair, but the circuit is very stable in the face of power supply and temperature changes. It has a good short-term frequency stability of 0.1 ppm. Its oscillation frequency is very high, however, at 301 ppm above series resonance. This is due to the low capacitance load on the crystal acting in series with the crystal's internal motional capacitance, reducing the total net series capacitance and raising the oscillation frequency.

The high resistance load circuit (Fig. 10.6a) turns out to be essentially the same as the low capacitance load circuit, but with poorer performance. The former oscillates at an even higher frequency than the low capacitance load circuit, at 671 ppm above series resonance. This is due to the very small capacitance load on the crystal.

Common base amplifier circuits (Figs. 10.7a and b and 10.8) give above average performance. Crystal waveforms and the short-term frequency stability are both very good. The crystal has very low source and load resistances, which give it its very good short-term frequency stability. The frequency is somewhat sensitive to temperature changes. The circuit oscillates exactly at series resonance.

Pierce circuits (Figs. 10.9a,d, and g and 10.10a) give outstanding performance. Crystal waveforms are good to very good. The short-term stability is 0.1 ppm, as good as any circuit tested, with the exception of the modified Meacham. The oscillation frequency is normally a little above (5–40 ppm) series resonance but can be set exactly at series resonance or even below it. The frequency sensitivity to power supply and temperature changes is very low, as good as any circuit tested. The circuits dissipate very little power in the crystal and provide a high output voltage at the same time. The reduced gain advantage of operating the Pierce without a series resistor (Fig. 10.11a) does not offer much in a discrete transistor circuit, but it does permit making a Pierce oscillator out of a CMOS inverter, which does not have enough gain for the standard Pierce circuit. Operating the Pierce at exact series resonance requires more parts in the circuit and does not seem to offer much advantage in exchange for the higher parts count.

The emitter coupled circuit (Fig. 10.12) gives average performance. Its measured performance is above average, but the sensitivity of its waveforms to stray capacitance effects brings its overall performance down to average. Its sensitivity to power supply and temperature changes is very low, and its short-term frequency stability is very good. One disadvantage of the circuit is its relatively high parts count.

Modified Meacham circuits (Figs. 10.13a,c, and d) give outstanding performance. Crystal waveforms are fair to good, and the short-term stability is 0.1 ppm or better, at the limit of available measuring equipment. Although it was not possible to measure short-term stability accurately, due to the limitations of the test equipment available, it appears to be better than that of any other circuit. The frequency changes very little when the power supply or temperature are changed. The circuit is complex, difficult to design, and has a high parts count. It operates at or near series resonance, depending on the tuning of its LC tank. Amplifier gain in this circuit directly affects short-term frequency stability: the higher the gain, the better the stability is. The maximum gain obtained in a stable two- or three-stage transistor amplifier varied from 28–100X, considerably less than the 300–422X obtained by Clapp and Meacham in their original circuits using a pentode vacuum tube amplifier.

12.3. SERIES-RESONANT OSCILLATORS USING ICs

The performance of series-resonant IC oscillators varies from above average to poor. The measured performance of a test circuit of each type is listed in Table 12.2; the data were obtained from the circuits shown in Figs. 11.1–11.7. The performance of these series-resonant IC oscillators is summarized in the following paragraphs.

The CMOS two-inverters circuit (4009 in Fig. 11.1) gives poor performance. It has good waveforms at the crystal, but its frequency is very sensitive to power supply and temperature changes. Its upper frequency limit is 300 kHz. The 74C04 (Fig. 11.2) also gives poor performance. It has good waveforms at the crystal, but its frequency is very sensitive to power supply changes. The 74C04's performance is slightly better than that of the 4009, and it has a higher upper frequency limit of 500 kHz.

TABLE 12.2 **TABLE 12.2** Performance of IC Oscillator Circuits

IC Number	Circuit	Type	Schematic in Figure	Useful Frequency Range	Measured Performance	
					Does Circuit Oscillate Without Crystal?	Frequency of Oscillation (MHz)
4009	Series resonance	CMOS-2 inverters	11.1	Below 300 kHz	No	0.199 993
74C04	Series resonance	CMOS-2 inverters	11.2	Below 500 kHz	No	0.199 995
7404	Series resonance	TTL-2 inverters	11.3a	800 kHz–3 MHz	Yes	0.999 999
74S04	Series resonance	TTL-2 inverters	11.3b	1–3 MHz	Yes	0.999 998
74LS04	Series resonance	TTL-2 inverters	11.3c	100 kHz–3 MHz	Yes	0.999 996
319	Series resonance	TTL-V. compar.	11.4	Below 1 MHz	Yes	0.999 981
9615	Series resonance	TTL-Line receiver	11.5	100 kHz–2 MHz	No	0.999 996
8820	Series resonance	TTL-Line receiver	11.6	100 kHz–1 MHz	No	0.999 984
10114	Series resonance	ECL-Line receiver	11.7a	500 kHz–10 MHz	No	1.000 001
10116	Series resonance	ECL-Line receiver	11.7a	1–20 MHz	No	1.000 001
10216	Series resonance	ECL-Line receiver	11.7a	1–20 MHz	No	1.000 001
10216	Series resonance	ECL-Line receiver	11.7c	1–20 MHz	No	19.999 773
10114	Meacham	ECL-Line receiver	11.11a	100 kHz–20 MHz	No	10.000 055
74C04	Pierce	CMOS-inverter	11.8	1 kHz–2 MHz	No	1.000 040
319	Pierce	TTL-V. compar.	11.9	10 kHz–2 MHz	Yes	1.000 001
10114	Pierce	ECL-Line receiver	11.10a	100 kHz–20 MHz	No	1.000 006

Waveforms at Crystal	Square Wave on/off Times (μsec; should be equal)	P.S. Sensitivity ($\Delta V_{cc} = 2$ V) Δf (ppm)	Circuit Temperature Sensitivity		Overall Performance	Remarks
			Freeze Δf (ppm)	Heat Δf (ppm)		
Good	2.4/2.6	13.	+3.	+12.	Poor	
Good	2.45/2.55	14.	+2.	−4.	Poor	
Good	0.49/0.51	2.	+0.5	0.0	Good	
Good	—	1.	—	—	Good	
Good	—	2.	—	—	Good	
Fair	0.60/0.40	5.	−0.7	−1.	Fair	
Very good	0.50/0.50	0.2	+0.3	−1.	Good	Low parts count
Fair	0.40/0.60	2.	+3.	−6.	Fair	
Very good	0.50/0.50	0.1	—	—	Very good	Recommended
Very good	0.50/0.50	0.4	—	—	Very good	Recommended
Very good	0.50/0.50	0.1	−0.1	−0.4	Very good	Recommended
Very good	0.025/0.025	0.7	—	—	Very good	Recommended
Fair	0.05/0.05	4.	—	—	Good	Complex circuit
Good	0.50/0.50	3.	+2.	−2.	Good	Low parts count
Good	0.60/0.40	1.	−0.3	−2.	Good	
Good	0.49/0.51	0.2	+0.8	−0.5	Very good	High parts count

(continued)

TABLE 12.2 (*continued*)

					Measured Performance	
IC Number	Circuit	Type	Schematic in Figure	Useful Frequency Range	Does Circuit Oscillate Without Crystal?	Frequency of Oscillation (MHz)
10216	Pierce	ECL-Line receiver	11.10c	100 kHz–20 MHz	No	20.000 525
7209	Pierce	CMOS-Special IC	11.12	4 kHz–10 MHz	No	1.000 077
7209	Pierce	CMOS-Special IC	11.12	4 kHz–10 MHz	No	10.006 329
74LS321	Common base	TTL-Special IC	11.13	1–20 MHz	No	1.000 006
74LS321	Common base	TTL-Special IC	11.13	1–20 MHz	No	19.999 080
SP705B	Common base	TTL-Special IC	11.14	1–10 MHz	No	1.000 000
SP705B	Common base	TTL-Special IC	11.14	1–10 MHz	No	9.998 560
12060	Common base	ECL-Special IC	11.15	100 kHz–2 MHz	No	0.100 003
12060	Common base	ECL-Special IC	11.15	100 kHz–2 MHz	No	1.999 428
12061	Common base	ECL-Special IC	11.15	2–20 MHz	No	2.000 000
12061	Common base	ECL-Special IC	11.15	2–20 MHz	No	19.992 953
LM375	Series resonance	Linear-special IC	11.16a	100 kHz–10 MHz	No	0.500 073
LM375	Series resonance	Linear-special IC	11.16b	100 kHz–10 MHz	Yes	10.000 338
SL680C	Emitter coupled	Linear-special IC	11.17a	2–20 MHz	No	1.999 986
SL680C	Emitter coupled	Linear-special IC	11.17a	2–20 MHz	No	19.999 001

Measured Performance

Waveforms at Crystal	Square Wave on/off Times (μsec; should be equal)	P.S. Sensitivity (ΔV_{cc} = 2 V) Δf (ppm)	Circuit Temperature Sensitivity		Overall Performance	Remarks
			Freeze Δf (ppm)	Heat Δf (ppm)		
Good	0.026/0.024	2.	—	—	Good	High parts count
Very good	0.48/0.52	1.	+0.7	−2.	Good	Low parts count
Very good	0.052/0.048	1.	−3.	−4.	Good	Low parts count
Poor	0.46/0.54	4.	+1.	−2.	Poor	
Poor	—	102.	—	—	Poor	
Poor	1.0/1.0	0.2	−0.2	−1.	Fair	
Poor	—	47.	—	—	Poor	
Poor	4.4/5.6	0.	0.	−1.	Poor	
Poor	0.22/0.28	10.	+180.	−150.	Poor	
Poor	0.23/0.27	0.2	+0.1	−0.2	Poor	
Poor	0.018/0.032	14.	+11.	−28.	Poor	
Good	0.95/1.05	0.2	−0.4	+2.	Good	
Very good	0.056/0.044	2.	—	—	Fair	
Very good	—	0.0	−2.	−2.	Good[a]	Sine wave output
Very good	—	3.	−1.	−12.	Fair[a]	Sine wave output

[a] Data at +6 VDC

The TTL two-inverters circuit (7404 in Fig. 11.3a) gives average performance. Waveforms at the crystal are good, and the frequency is reasonably independent of power supply and temperature changes. The 74S04 offers no advantages over the 7404, but the 74LS04 does. The 74LS04 can be used at lower frequencies (down to 100 kHz), but its frequency is a little more sensitive to power supply changes. All three TTL inverters oscillate at a spurious frequency when the crystal is removed from the circuit, a practical disadvantage. The upper frequency limit for all three TTL inverters is about 3 MHz. This is controlled by the crystal's power dissipation limit rather than by the inverters themselves.

The TTL voltage comparator circuit (LM319 in Fig. 11.4) gives below average performance. Waveforms at the crystal are only fair, and the frequency is rather sensitive to power supply voltage changes. The crystal's source and load resistances are a little high, reducing the short-term frequency stability. The circuit's upper frequency limit is 1 MHz.

As to the two TTL receiver circuits (9615 and 8820 in Figs. 11.5 and 11.6), the performance of the 9615 is above average. Waveforms at the crystal are very good, and its frequency is relatively insensitive to power supply and temperature changes. The 9615 has a low parts count and an upper frequency limit of 2 MHz. The performance of the 8820 is below average. Crystal waveforms are only fair, its frequency is sensitive to temperature changes, and the crystal's load resistance has to be relatively high, reducing its short-term frequency stability. Its upper frequency limit is 1 MHz.

All three of the ECL receivers (10114, 10116, and 10216 in Figs. 11.7a and c) give above average performance as series-resonant circuits. Crystal waveforms are very good, and the frequency is relatively independent of power supply and temperature changes. The crystal's source and load resistances are low, giving good short-term frequency stability. The upper frequency limit is at least 20 MHz. One drawback for TTL use is that they need a buffer to convert the oscillators' ECL output to the TTL format.

12.4. PIERCE OSCILLATORS USING ICs

Pierce-IC oscillators give above average to average performance. The measured performance of a test circuit of each type is listed in Table 12.2. The data were obtained from the circuits in Figs. 11.8–11.10. The performance of Pierce-IC oscillators is summarized in the following paragraphs.

The Pierce-CMOS inverter circuit (74C04 in Fig. 11.8) gives average performance. Crystal waveforms are good, and the oscillation frequency is reasonably independent of power supply and temperature changes. Maximum frequency for the Pierce-CMOS circuit is about 1 MHz for most manufacturers' CMOS (B series), 2 MHz for National Semiconductor's 74C series, and 5 MHz for Solid State Scientific's 4000A/B series CMOS.

The Pierce-TTL circuit (Fig. 11.9) uses an LM319 voltage comparator and gives above average performance. Crystal waveforms are good, and the oscillation frequency is reasonably independent of power supply and temperature changes. A voltage comparator is the only TTL circuit that has enough gain to make a Pierce oscillator. Maximum frequency for the voltage comparator circuit is about 2 MHz. Although Pierce circuits normally operate at 5–40 ppm above series resonance, the oscillation frequency in the test circuit was only 1 ppm above series resonance, due to the large 60-nsec time delay in the voltage comparator.

Pierce-ECL circuits (10114, 10116, and 10216 in Figs. 11.10a and c) give above average performance at 1 MHz and average performance at 20 MHz. Crystal waveforms are good at both frequencies, and at 1 MHz, the frequency is almost completely independent of power supply and temperature changes. The three receivers in a DIP are connected in series to get enough gain for the Pierce circuit. The 10114 is used at 1 MHz and the 10116 or 10216 at 20 MHz. When used to drive TTL circuitry, the parts count is relatively high. This is due to the large number of emitter pull-down resistors used in the circuit and the ECL-to-TTL interface circuit that is needed at the output.

12.5. MEACHAM OSCILLATORS USING ICs

The Meacham-ECL circuit (Fig. 11.11a) is a full-bridge circuit giving above average performance. Its short-term stability of 0.1 ppm is very good, at the limit of available measuring equipment. The ECL output stage has a difficult task driving the low 5-Ω resistance R_s of the crystal at 10 MHz, and this results in only fair waveforms at the crystal and increases the frequency sensitivity to power supply changes. Both crystal waveform and power supply sensitivity would improve at frequencies lower than 10 MHz, where the crystal's internal series resistance R_s would be higher and easier to drive.

The modified Meacham-ECL half-bridge circuit (Fig. 11.11c) performs just as well as the full-bridge circuit. But since the full-bridge circuit uses only one more resistor and can cancel out drive-source variations, it has an advantage over the half-bridge circuit.

12.6. SPECIAL OSCILLATOR ICs

As a group, ICs that are specifically designed for use as crystal oscillator circuits do not perform very well when compared with discrete transistor circuits. The special oscillator ICs generally try to cover a wide range of frequencies with a fixed circuit, and this is very difficult to do. As a rule, the ICs work best at the low end of their frequency range and poorest at the high end. Many of them drive the crystal with a badly distorted waveform. Their general performance ranges from average to poor. Special oscillator ICs can usually provide reasonable source and load resistances for the crystal at the low-frequency end of their range, but source and load resistances are invariably too high for high-frequency operation, and, hence, their short-term stability is not too good at the higher frequencies. To maintain a perspective, poor does not mean unacceptable. The label poor performance here is with respect to what can be done with discrete transistor circuits. Even the poorest crystal oscillator circuit will provide a more stable frequency source than an LC-type oscillator circuit.

The measured performance of a test circuit of each type is listed in Table 12.2. The data were taken from the circuits shown in Figs. 11.12–11.17. The performance of the special oscillator ICs is summarized in the following paragraphs.

The 7209 (CMOS) uses the Pierce circuit and operates from at least 4 kHz up to 10 MHz. It gives good performance at 1 MHz and 10 MHz. Crystal waveforms are very good, and the frequency is reasonably independent of power supply and temperature changes. And as with any Pierce circuit, capacitors C_1 and C_2 in the circuit should be changed when the frequency is changed.

The 74LS321 (TTL) uses a variation of the common base amplifier circuit and operates from 1–20 MHz. Performance is poor at 1 MHz and 20 MHz. The circuit has two main drawbacks. The waveform driving the crystal is poor, and an inductor is used in the circuit when it is not necessary (from a design viewpoint). The frequency is reasonably independent of power supply and temperature changes at 1 MHz. At 20 MHz, the frequency drifts 1 ppm short term and changes a large 102 ppm when the power-supply voltage changes from 4 to 6 V.

The SP705B (TTL) uses the common base amplifier circuit and operates from 1–10 MHz. It gives fair performance at 1 MHz but is poor at 10

MHz. Crystal waveforms are distorted. At 1 MHz, the frequency is relatively independent of power supply and temperature changes, but at 10 MHz, the frequency changes a large 47 ppm when the power supply voltage is changed from 4 to 6 V.

Both the 12060 and the 12061 (ECL) use a variation of the common base amplifier circuit, and cover frequency ranges of 100 kHz–2 MHz and 2–20 MHz, respectively. Sine wave, ECL, and TTL outputs are provided. The performance of the 12060 is poor at both 100 kHz and 2 MHz. Crystal waveforms are distorted. The frequency is relatively independent of power supply and temperature changes at 100 kHz, but changes a large 150–180 ppm with temperature at 2 MHz. The performance of the 12061 is poor at both 2 and 20 MHz. Crystal waveforms are distorted. At 2 MHz, its frequency is relatively independent of power supply and temperature changes. But at 20 MHz, it is sensitive to power supply and temperature changes, changing 14 ppm when the power supply is changed from 4 to 6 V and changing 28 ppm when heated above ambient.

The LM375 (LINEAR) uses the series-resonant circuit and can be used over a frequency range of 100 kHz–10 MHz. Above 500 kHz, a tuned LC tank is required for the oscillator load. The LM375 has both sine wave and TTL outputs, and gives good performance at and below 500 kHz with a resistive oscillator load. Crystal waveforms are good, and the frequency is relatively independent of power supply and temperature changes. Above 500 kHz, the LM375's performance is only fair, because of the unnecessary use (from a design viewpoint) of an LC tank and because it oscillates spuriously with the crystal removed from the circuit.

The SL680C (LINEAR) uses the emitter coupled circuit and operates at frequencies from 2–20 MHz. The SL680C has a sine wave output only. It is designed for a power supply voltage of +6 to +10 VDC but will operate at +5 V if a clipped sine wave output is acceptable. The SL680C's performance is good at 2 MHz and fair at 20 MHz. The crystal's waveform is a nice sine wave. At 2 MHz, its frequency is relatively independent of power supply and temperature changes. But at 20 MHz, the frequency is sensitive to temperature, changing 12 ppm when the IC is heated above ambient.

12.7. HARMONIC OSCILLATORS

Performance of the VHF harmonic circuits ranges from above average to below average. The measured performance of harmonic circuits is listed in Table 12.3; the data were taken from the circuits in Figs. 10.14–10.25,

TABLE 12.3 Performance of Harmonic Oscillator Circuits

Circuit	Type	Schematic in Figure	Useful Frequency Range	Measured Performance	
				Harmonic	Does Circuit Oscillate Without Crystal?
Colpitts	Discrete transistor	10.14	200 kHz–100 MHz	3rd	No
Butler common base, C-tap	Discrete transistor	10.15	15–100 MHz	3rd	No
Butler common base, L-tap	Discrete transistor	10.16	15–50 MHz	3rd	No
Butler common base	Discrete transistor	10.17	15–100 MHz	3rd	No
Butler common base, C-tap	Discrete transistor	10.18	15–100 MHz	5th	No
Butler common base, L-tap	Discrete transistor	10.19	70–200 MHz	5th	—
Butler emitter follower, C-tap	Discrete transistor	10.20	15–200 MHz	3rd	No
Butler emitter follower, L-tap	Discrete transistor	10.21	15–200 MHz	3rd	No
Butler emitter follower	Discrete transistor	10.22	15–200 MHz	3rd	No
Butler emitter follower, C-tap	Discrete transistor	10.23	15–200 MHz	5th	No
Butler emitter follower, L-tap	Discrete transistor	10.24	70–200 MHz	5th	—
Butler emitter follower, IC	ECL (10216)	11.18	15–100 MHz	5th	No
Pierce	Discrete transistor	10.25	20–100 MHz	5th	No

and Fig. 11.18. Figure 11.18 is the only harmonic oscillator using an IC; the others use discrete transistors. Performance of the harmonic circuits is summarized in the following paragraphs.

The Butler common base circuit gives below average performance. Crystal waveforms are good, but its frequency sensitivity to power supply and temperature changes is only fair. The collector current must be held at a certain fixed value or the circuit will not oscillate. The circuit

Measured Performance						
Frequency of Oscillation (MHz)	Waveforms at Crystal	P.S. Sensitivity ($\Delta V_{cc} = 2$ V) Δf (ppm)	Circuit Temperature Sensitivity		Overall Performance	Remarks
			Freeze Δf (ppm)	Heat Δf (ppm)		
20.000 706	Good	6.	−4.	+1.	Fair	
20.000 022	Good	3.	−0.1	−4.	Poor–fair	Parasitics
19.999 918	Fair	0.3	+0.3	−4.	Fair	
50.000 306	Good	0.5	—	—	Poor–fair	Parasitics
100.001 281	Good	0.3	—	—	Poor–fair	Parasitics
100.000 937	Good	0.5	—	—	Poor	Not recommended
20.000 051	Very good	0.3	+0.6	−4.	Very good	Recommended
19.999 958	Very good	0.4	+0.8	−3.	Very good	Recommended
50.000 042	Good	2.	—	—	Very good	Recommended
100.001 513	Good	2.	—	—	Very good	Recommended
99.996 603	Good	5.	—	—	Poor	Not recommended
100.000 847	Good	2.	−3.	−3.	Good	
99.999 171	Good	2.	—	—	Good	

has a nasty parasitic oscillation problem if a capacitive tap is used on the LC tank, but it goes away if an inductive tap is used. With a capacitive tap, the circuit operates slightly above or at series resonance. With an inductive tap, the circuit operates slightly below series resonance.

The Butler emitter follower circuit gives above average performance. Crystal waveforms are good, and there are no parasitics of any kind. Its frequency is reasonably independent of power supply changes, but it does vary some with temperature changes. The circuit is easy to set up and tune. The inductive tap does not offer any advantages over a capacitive tap in this circuit. With a capacitive tap, the circuit operates slightly above or at series resonance. With an inductive tap, the circuit operates slightly below resonance. An ECL line receiver (10216 in Fig. 11.18) can be used for the amplifier in the Butler emitter follower circuit, and will give essentially the same performance as a discrete transistor amplifier.

Starting above 70 MHz or so, where an inductor must be put across the crystal to tune out the capacitive effect of the crystal's terminal capacitance C_0, the capacitive tap is easier to work with than the inductive tap. With the inductive tap, the crystal's shunt inductor introduces an inconvenient DC circuit connection, which has to be broken by adding a series capacitor. Adding a series capacitor at these high frequencies is undesirable because the capacitor's leads add inductance to the circuit.

The Pierce circuit (Fig. 10.25), using a resonant LC tank in its amplifier, gives above average performance at 100 MHz. Crystal waveforms are very good, and the frequency is relatively insensitive to power supply voltage changes. The circuit's short-term frequency stability is very good. A drawback to this circuit is its high parts count.

The Colpitts circuit (Fig. 10.14), using an inductor for the emitter load, gives average performance at 20 MHz. Crystal waveform is good, but the frequency is somewhat sensitive to power supply changes. The circuit has a low parts count, a practical advantage.

12.8. WHICH IS THE BEST CIRCUIT?

Which is the best circuit? There are two that stand out above the rest: the modified Meacham and the Pierce. The modified Meacham has the best short-term frequency stability. Analytically, it has the steepest curves of phase shift with frequency. And experimentally, its short-term stability of 0.1 ppm (or better) was at the limit of available measuring equipment and appeared to be better than that of any other circuit. The modified Meacham has three disadvantages that partially offset its outstanding frequency stability. The circuit is complex; it has a high parts count; and it is difficult to design.

The Pierce stands out on almost every count. It has good waveforms at the crystal, a frequency that is relatively independent of power supply and temperature changes, very good short-term frequency stability, high output voltage, low crystal dissipation, low cost, and it is usable at any frequency from the highest to the lowest. The only disadvantage of the

TABLE 12.4
Relative Performance of Circuit Types

Relative Performance	Circuit
Outstanding	Modified Meacham Pierce
Above average	Butler emitter follower (harmonic) Common base amplifier-discrete transistors Series-resonant-ECL
Average	Emitter coupled Colpitts TTL two-inverters Low capacitance load
Below average	High-resistance load Butler common base (harmonic) CMOS two-inverters
Poor	Special oscillator ICs Miller

Pierce is that its frequency stability is a little less than that of the modified Meacham.

Above 20 MHz, where harmonic circuits must be used, the Butler emitter follower is the best circuit. It is a simple, low cost, easy to tune circuit, with good waveforms at the crystal. It has no parasitics, and its frequency is relatively independent of power supply changes. The Pierce with a tuned LC tank in its amplifier also works well as a harmonic oscillator, but it has a relatively high parts count.

Table 12.4 lists the relative performance of various circuit types. The Pierce and modified Meacham are in the outstanding group, for the reasons just given.

In the above average group are the Butler emitter follower (harmonic), common base amplifier (discrete transistors), and series-resonant-ECL circuits. All these circuits perform very well, with good frequency stability and very good waveforms at the crystal.

In the average group are the emitter coupled, Colpitts, TTL two-inverters, and low capacitance load circuits.

In the below average group are the high resistance load, Butler common base (harmonic), and CMOS two-inverters circuits. The high resistance load circuit has the disadvantage of an oscillation frequency way above series resonance. The Butler common base (harmonic) circuit suffers from bad parasitics. And the CMOS two-inverters circuit has the disadvantage that its frequency is too sensitive to power supply changes.

In the poor performance group are the special oscillator ICs and the Miller circuit. The special oscillator ICs actually fall into more than one group, but the majority of them fall into the poor performance group because of poor crystal waveforms and a frequency that is too sensitive to power supply and temperature changes. The Miller circuit has bad crystal waveforms and an unstable frequency. To maintain perspective, labeling the performance of one circuit as poor with respect to another circuit is a relative matter. In this case, it means poor with respect to what can be done with a discrete transistor circuit. It is worth repeating that even the poorest crystal oscillator circuit will provide a more stable frequency than an LC-type oscillator circuit.

CHAPTER THIRTEEN

OPTIMIZING THE OSCILLATOR CIRCUIT

This chapter describes how to select an oscillator circuit for a particular application. It also summarizes the most important oscillator design characteristics to aid those who would like to design their own oscillator circuits.

13.1. SELECTING A CIRCUIT

What circuit should be selected depends on the application. If the best short-term stability without regard to other circuit characteristics is needed, then the modified Meacham circuit is the best choice. But it will be necessary to put up with the Meacham's drawbacks of circuit complexity, the difficulty of designing a stable circuit, and a high parts count. (An alternative circuit that is easier to design and gives performance equal to the modified Meacham is the RLC half-bridge, which is described in the Appendix.) If very good short-term stability is required, but other circuit characteristics such as simplicity and ease of design are also important, then the Pierce is a good choice. The Pierce can be used at any frequency from the highest to the lowest, fundamental or harmonic, as shown by the assortment of Pierce schematics in this book.

Or, if harmonic operation above 20 MHz, with above average performance and reasonably few parts is needed, the Butler emitter follower circuit is the one to pick. If the bare minimum number of parts is a requisite and performance requirements can be relaxed a little, then the Colpitts, either fundamental or harmonic, is the one to pick.

A discrete transistor circuit will usually give better performance than an IC circuit. This is because it is easier to control the crystal's source

215

and load resistances, the gain, and signal amplitude in a discrete transistor circuit. The discrete transistor amplifier usually has less time delay in it, as well, since it normally has only one or two transistors.

On the other hand, oscillators using ICs are frequently cheaper when assembly labor costs are included. They also interface more easily with digital circuitry. And although their performance is generally less than that of a discrete transistor circuit, it is still better than what is needed for many types of digital circuitry.

In CMOS, the Pierce inverter circuit works well over the 1 kHz–2 MHz frequency range and requires only two inverters. From 4 kHz–10 MHz, the 7209 special oscillator IC, which also uses the Pierce inverter circuit, can be used.

In TTL below 3 MHz, the series-resonant two-inverters circuit gives good performance over the 100 kHz–3 MHz frequency range as long as the circuit's spurious oscillation problem with the crystal out of the circuit can be tolerated. In TTL above 3 MHz, either the series-resonant circuit using an ECL line receiver or the Pierce-ECL circuit would be a good choice. A TTL buffer circuit similar to those shown in the oscillator schematics is required for these above-3 MHz circuits.

In ECL below 20 MHz, the series-resonant line receiver circuit or the Pierce-ECL circuit would be a good selection, covering a frequency range of 100 kHz–20 MHz. In ECL above 20 MHz, the Butler emitter follower circuit (harmonic) using the 10216 line receiver would be a good circuit to use.

13.2. CIRCUIT DESIGN

The design of a crystal oscillator circuit is dominated by the crystal's internal series resistance R_s, far more than by any other factor. For a typical quartz crystal in a gas-filled container, the crystal's internal series resistance varies from a high of 200K Ω at 1 kHz to a low of 10 Ω at 20 MHz. For the best short-term frequency stability, the equivalent series load resistance seen by the crystal should be equal to or somewhat less than the crystal's internal series resistance R_s. To meet this crystal need, the circuit's impedance level has to vary over a wide range—high impedance at low frequencies, and low impedance at high frequencies. It is this characteristic that leads to such a wide variety of circuits over the frequency range.

In calculating the crystal's load, the crystal's shunt terminal capacitance C_0 of about 5 pF should be included as part of that load rather than as part of the frequency determining L_x and C_x elements in the crystal. Since the terminal capacitance C_0 is in parallel with the actual load resistance (or capacitance), a parallel-to-series network conversion is performed to find the equivalent series load resistance that is to be minimized. Good in-circuit Q can be obtained with either a high or low value of parallel load resistance across the crystal terminals. For the best Q, this parallel load resistance should be two to three orders of magnitude greater than or less than the impedance of the total shunt capacitance across the crystal terminals. Figure 6.4 shows graphically these minimum and maximum parallel load resistances that will give good in-circuit Q as a function of frequency. The graph in Fig. 6.4 assumes that the crystal's total shunt capacitance is just the shunt capacitance C_0 of the crystal itself (about 5 pF), which is the usual case.

The oscillator circuit should contain some means of ensuring that the amplifier is biased "on" at startup and is not in a biased "off" state, which would prevent oscillation from starting when power is applied. This is an essential element in any good oscillator circuit.

If the crystal is removed from the circuit or becomes defective, the circuit should not oscillate. Some circuits, like the TTL two-inverters circuit, continue to oscillate (spuriously) when the crystal is removed; this is poor design.

In general, the time delay in the oscillator's amplifier should be minimized, since it causes frequency shifts when the amplifier's temperature changes. The greater the amplifier's time delay as a percentage of the period of oscillation, the greater the frequency shifts with temperature changes. The square wave driving the crystal should be a good square wave, with a 50/50 on-off ratio and a rise time that is not too slow or too fast. The amplifier's frequency response and rise time should not be way beyond the oscillation frequency either. If they are, then multiple on-off switchings due to noise will occur in the amplifier at each zero crossing of the sine wave out of the crystal. A desirable delay and rise and fall time seems to be about 2 percent of the total period of oscillation.

It is worth repeating that both sine and square wave outputs are available from most oscillator circuits. The square wave is on the driving side of the crystal, and the sine wave is on the output side.

REFERENCES

1. J. M. Miller, Piezo Electric Oscillation Generator. U.S. Patent #1,756,000, April 1930. Both Miller and Pierce circuits.
2. G. W. Pierce, Electrical System. U.S. Patent #1,789,496, January 1931. Both Pierce and Miller circuits.
3. G. W. Pierce, Electrical System. U.S. Patent #2,133,642, October 1938. Both Pierce and Miller circuits.
4. S. Sabaroff, Voltage Stabilized High Frequency Crystal Oscillator Circuit. *Proc. IRE* **25**(5), 623–629 (1937). Quartz crystal version of Colpitts LC oscillator.
5. L. A. Meacham, Bridge-Stabilized Oscillator, *Proc. IRE* **26**(10), 1278–1294 (1938). Resistance bridge circuit.
6. F. Butler, Series Resonant Crystal Oscillators. *Wireless Eng.* **23**(6), 157–160 (1946). VHF harmonic circuits.
7. H. Goldberg and E. Crosby, Jr., Series Mode Crystal Circuits. *TELE-TECH*, 24–27 and 86 (May 1948). Cathode coupled circuits.
8. W. A. Edson, W. Clary, and J. Hogg, *High Frequency Crystal-Controlled Oscillator Circuits*. Final Report, Project 131-45, December 1950. Georgia Institute of Technology, State Engineering Experiment Station, Atlanta, Georgia. C.A.D.O. No. EEL-C4971 and T.I. 108261. VHF harmonic circuits.
9. W. A. Edson, *Vacuum Tube Oscillators*. Wiley, New York, 1953. Classic reference on oscillator circuits.
10. D. Firth, *Quartz Crystal Oscillator Circuits Design Handbook*, March 1965, ASTIA AD460377. Best reference on Pierce circuit and Butler common base harmonic circuit.
11. A. W. Warner, Design and Performance of Ultraprecise 2.5 mc Quartz Crystal Units. *BSTJ* **39**(5), 1193–1217 (1960).

12. A. W. Warner, Frequency Aging of High-Frequency Plated Crystal Units. *Proc. IRE* **43**(7), 790–792 (1952).

13. H. E. Bömmel, W. P. Mason, and A. W. Warner, Experimental Evidence for Dislocations in Crystalline Quartz. *Phys. Rev.* **99**(6), 1894–1896 (1955).

14. H. E. Bömmel, W. P. Mason, and A. W. Warner, Dislocations, Relaxations, and Anelasticity of Crystal Quartz. *Phys. Rev.* **102**(1), 64–71 (1956).

15. R. Harrison, Survey of Crystal Oscillators, *Ham Radio Magazine*, 10–22 (March 1976).

16. H. Bahadur and R. Parshad, Operation of Quartz Crystals in Their Overtones: New Methods. *Indian J. Pure Appl. Phys.* **13**, 862–865 (1975). Harmonic operation of Colpitts with resistive load on emitter.

17. E. J. Post and H. F. Pit, Alternate Ways in the Analysis of a Feedback Oscillator and Its Application. *Proc. IRE* **39**(2), 169–174 (1951). Analysis of Meacham circuit.

18. J. K. Clapp, Bridge-Controlled Oscillator. *Gen. Radio Exp.* **18**(11), 1–4 (April 1944); **18**(12), 6–8 (May 1944). Meacham circuit without transformers.

19. S. D. Culp, Crystal Oscillator Uses Logic Gates. *EEE*, 87 (July 1970). TTL inverter circuit.

20. B. Blood, Interfacing with MECL 10,000 Integrated Circuits. Motorola Application Note An-720, February 1974.

BIBLIOGRAPHY

Anderson, T. C. and G. F. Merrill, Crystal-Controlled Primary Frequency Standards: Latest Advances for Long Term Stability. *IRE Trans. Instrum.*, 136–140 (September 1960).

Buchanan, J. P., *Handbook of Piezoelectric Crystals for Radio Equipment Designers*, October 1956, ASTIA AD110448. Quartz crystals and oscillator circuits.

Felch, E. P. and J. O. Israel, Simple Circuit for Frequency Standards Employing Overtone Crystals. *Proc. IRE* **43**(5), 596–603 (1955).

Gerber, E. and R. Sykes, State of the Art—Quartz Crystal Units and Oscillators. *Proc. IEEE* **54**(2), 103–116 (1966).

Gruen, H. E. and A. O. Plait, *A Study of Crystal Oscillator Circuits*. Final Report, Armour Research Foundation, August 1957, ASTIA AD149085. Wide variety of circuits.

Hafner, E., Crystal Resonators. *IEEE Trans. Sonics Ultra-sonics* **SU-21**(4), 220–236 (October 1974).

Lane, M., *Transistor Crystal Oscillators to Cover Frequency Range 1 kHz–100 MHz*, Report No. 6513, September 1970. Australian Post Office Research Laboratories, 59 Little Collins St., Melbourne, Victoria, Australia 3000.

Pustarfi, H. S., Improved 5 mHz Reference Oscillator for Time and Frequency Standard Applications. *IEEE Trans.* **IM-15**(4), 196–200 (December 1966).

Smith, W. L., Miniature Transistorized Crystal-Controlled Precision Oscillators. *IRE Trans. Instrum.*, 141–148 (September 1960).

Smith, W. L., Precision Quartz Crystal Controlled Oscillators Using Transistor Circuits. *Bell Labs Record* **42**(8), 273–279 (1964).

Sykes, R. A., High Frequency Plated Quartz Crystal Units. *Proc. IRE* **36**(1), 194–197 (1948).

Warner, A. W., High Frequency Crystal Units for Primary Frequency Standards. *Proc. IRE* **40**(9), 1030–1033 (1952).

RLC HALF-BRIDGE CIRCUIT

This circuit is a late improvement on the already outstanding modified Meacham, and since it performs equally well, it is included here as an Appendix.

The modified Meacham circuit described in Section 5.11 gives outstanding performance, but it is very difficult to design. Its design can be made easier by moving the amplifier's LC network over to the resistive arm of the half-bridge. All the frequency controlling elements are then in the bridge arms, and the amplifier can have a flat frequency response. A wide range of noninverting amplifier designs can be used with this new circuit arrangement.

A simplified schematic of the RLC half-bridge circuit is shown in Fig. A.1. The two bridge arms are driven out-of-phase, with the transistor operating as a split-load phase inverter. The operation of the bridge is described in detail in Sections 5.11 and 7.5, but in essence the out-of-phase signal through the resistive bridge arm R_1 cancels out part of the crystal's internal resistance R_s. This effectively increases the crystal's in-circuit Q, which in turn increases the short-term frequency stability. And the higher the amplifier's gain, the more the crystal's in-circuit Q can be increased.

Figure A.2 shows the gain and phase shift characteristics of the half-bridge in the RLC half-bridge circuit. L_1 and C_1 are series resonant at the crystal's fundamental frequency. The overall broad peak of the gain curve is due to the series resonance of L_1 and C_1, and the sharp "hole" or slot at the peak is due to the crystal's series resonance. The phase shift through the bridge changes from +270° (lead) below the resonant frequency to −270° (lag) above resonance.

The design of the RLC half-bridge circuit is as follows. In Fig. A.1, R_1 has the smallest possible value that will still let the circuit oscillate, and

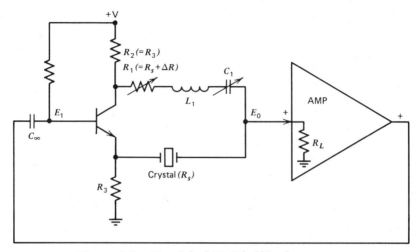

Figure A.1. Simplified RLC half-bridge circuit.

allow the maximum crystal in-circuit Q to be obtained (the circuit will not oscillate if R_1 is less than R_s, except spuriously). This requires the highest possible amplifier gain without the amplifier oscillating spuriously. C_1 is tuned to resonance with L_1 at the crystal's fundamental frequency. C_1 can be varied slightly from its resonance value to trim the crystal's oscillation frequency.

A high L_1/C_1 ratio is desirable. A low L_1/C_1 ratio gives a broad frequency transmission band to the half-bridge, and the crystal then oscillates at its 3rd or 5th harmonic where the bridge gain is higher, rather than at its fundamental frequency. A high L_1/C_1 ratio gives a narrow frequency transmission band, so that the bridge gain at the crystal's 3rd and

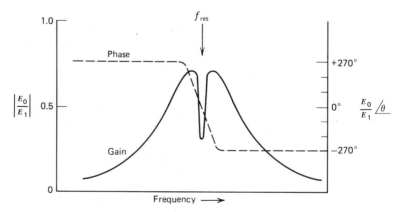

Figure A.2. Gain and phase characteristics of the half-bridge in Fig. A.1.

5th harmonics is too low for oscillation, and the crystal then has to oscillate at its fundamental frequency. The inductance L_1 should be reasonably large, with its maximum value limited by its internal AC resistance. The internal AC resistance of L_1 should be less than the crystal's internal resistance R_s, so as not to limit the maximum crystal Q obtainable in the circuit.

The bridge load resistance R_L in Fig. A.1 should not have too high a value. R_L should be about 2–10 times the crystal's internal series resistance R_s. If R_L is much larger than this, the circuit will not be stable when R_1 is set less than R_s to check the amplifier's stability. And although it is not shown in Fig. A.1, a small capacitance equal to (or slightly greater than) the crystal's external terminal capacitance C_0 is tied across the $R_1 L_1 C_1$ bridge arm to balance out the crystal's terminal shunt capacitance C_0.

Figure A.3 shows a schematic of the RLC half-bridge at 1 MHz. The amplifier uses two transistors in an emitter coupled configuration, with an emitter follower at the output. Q_2 provides a relatively high load resistance to the bridge at point A, so that the bridge load resistance R_L is primarily determined by the emitter biasing resistor R_2. Two diodes in parallel (D_1-D_2) with reversed polarity provide an amplitude clamp to drive the crystal with a low-excitation, constant-amplitude signal. The amplifier has a gain of $50\times$ from point A to point B in Fig. A.3. The bridge operates with a $2:1$ voltage excitation ratio between the two bridge arms. With a $2:1$ half-bridge, the theoretical minimum value for R_1 is $R_s/2$, or 120 Ω. The effective value of R_1 has to include the AC resistance of L_1 (60 Ω). This gives a ratio of the practical to theoretical minimum values for R_1 of $(110 + 60)/120 = 1.4$, a desirably low ratio (1.0 is the unattainable minimum, corresponding to infinite Q).

The frequency changes 0.0 ppm when the power supply voltage is changed from 4 to 6 V, but this is dependent on the tuning of C_1. The short-term frequency stability measured 0.1 ppm at the limit of the measuring equipment available. An oddity of the circuit is that C_2 has to be greater than 17 pF, much more than the required bridge balancing value of $2C_0$ (6 pF), to make the circuit stable and prevent spurious oscillation when R_1 is set less than the minimum value for fundamental oscillation.

Figure A.4 shows a schematic of the RLC half-bridge at 100 kHz. This circuit is similar to the 1 MHz circuit in Fig. A.3. The frequency changes 0.4 ppm when the power supply voltage is changed from 4 to 6 V, but this is dependent on the tuning of C_1. The short-term frequency stability measured 0.1 ppm, at the limit of the measuring equipment available. The amplifier gain from point A to point B in Fig. A.4 is $57\times$. The theoretical minimum value of R_1 in this circuit is $R_s/2$, or 200 Ω. This

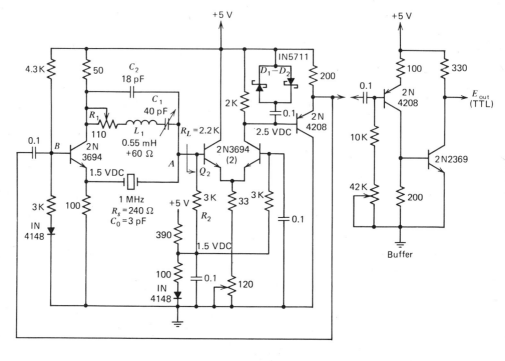

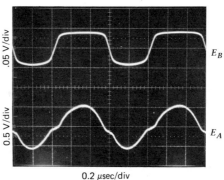

0.2 μsec/div

Figure A.3. RLC half-bridge at 1 MHz.

gives a ratio of the practical to theoretical minimum values for R_1, including the AC resistance of L_1, of $(420 + 11)/200 = 2.1$. $R_3 C_3$ prevents parasitic oscillation in the circuit. C_2 has to be at least 19 pF, slightly greater than the required bridge balancing value of $2C_0$ (16 pF), to make the circuit stable and prevent spurious oscillation when R_1 is set less than the minimum value for fundamental oscillation.

Figure A.5 shows a schematic of the RLC half-bridge at 10 MHz. The

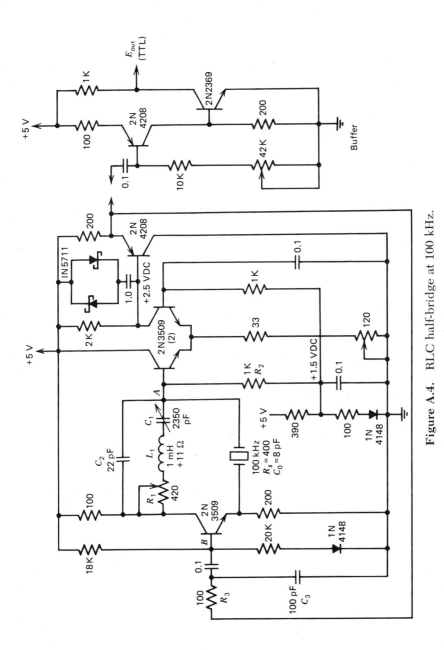

Figure A.4. RLC half-bridge at 100 kHz.

227

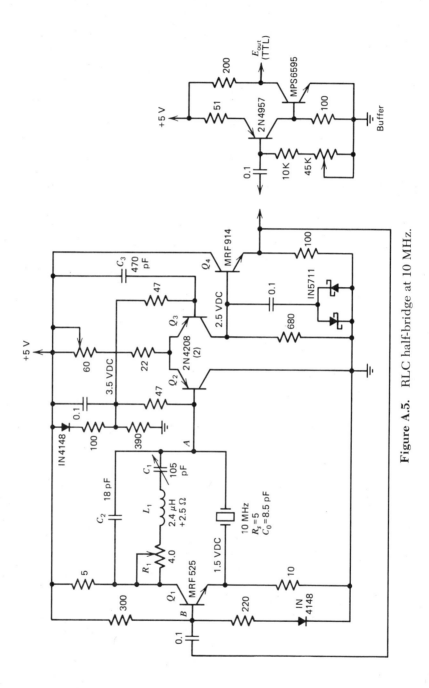

Figure A.5. RLC half-bridge at 10 MHz.

228

base input resistance of the *npn* phase inverter Q_1 is very low and is best driven by an *npn* type of emitter follower. The emitter coupled amplifier Q_2-Q_3 uses *pnp* transistors, so that an *npn* transistor can be used for the emitter follower Q_4. The amplifier gain from point A to point B in Fig. A.5 is only 17× and is limited by the low gain of the high-frequency *pnp* transistors available and the loss in gain from C_3's phase lead correction. The amplifier has a phase lag of 29°, which is compensated to zero by 29° of phase lead from C_3. The frequency changes 1.2 ppm when the power supply voltage is changed from 4 to 6 V. The short-term frequency stability measured 0.1 ppm, at the limit of the measuring equipment available. The theoretical minimum value of R_1 in this circuit is $R_s/2$, or 2.5 Ω. This gives a ratio of the practical to theoretical minimum values for R_1, including the AC resistance of L_1, of (4 + 2.5)/2.5 = 2.6. A heat sink is required on Q_1 in Fig. A.5.

The crystal waveforms vary from good to very good in the three circuits. All three circuits are stable and do not oscillate spuriously when the resistance R_1 is set at 0 Ω, that is, at less than the minimum value for oscillation, $R_s/2$. The stability margin is somewhat small in the 100-kHz and 10-MHz circuits, but the test shows that the amplifier circuits are stable. In addition, the three circuits are stable and do not oscillate when the crystals are removed from the circuits. No temperature tests have been made on the circuits.

As can be seen from the above data, the RLC half-bridge gives the same outstanding performance as the modified Meacham. It does this with a reasonably simple "flat amplifier" design, compared to the much more difficult tuned amplifier circuit that's used in the modified Meacham. Adding L_1C_1 to the bridge arm makes the half-bridge part of the circuit a little more complex, but the impact is not nearly as great as the elimination of the tuned amplifier. Because it gives the same performance with a simpler circuit, the RLC half-bridge is an improvement on the modified Meacham circuit.

INDEX